THE ROCKY MOUNTAINS

THE ROCKY MOUNTAINS

by

WALLACE W. ATWOOD
President, Clark University

THIRD VOLUME IN THE
AMERICAN MOUNTAIN SERIES
EDITED BY RODERICK PEATTIE

THE VANGUARD PRESS

NEW YORK

MANUFACTURED IN THE UNITED STATES OF AMERICA
BY H. WOLFF, NEW YORK, N. Y.

TO

HARRIET T. B. ATWOOD,

to the other members of my family, and to more
than one hundred students who have accompanied
me on one or more of my pack-train expeditions
through the Rocky Mountains

ACKNOWLEDGMENTS

In the preparation of this book I have had an unusual amount of help from various sources. I am deeply appreciative of the artistic sketches which Eugene Kingman has made. He was with me on two long pack-train expeditions and is very familiar with camp life and the atmosphere in high mountain regions. Mr. Erwin Raisz has helped me a great many times in making technical drawings for scientific publications. This time he has prepared eight very attractive sketches and the relief map of the Rocky Mountains which I think add much of value to the book.

When the first draft of the manuscript was ready Mrs. S. J. Brandenburg, who has had wide experience in writing, went over all of the material very critically and made many helpful suggestions.

Miss Helen J. Elliott, of the library staff at Clark University, has been my chief assistant in research work and has checked on many of the statistical and historical facts which are incorporated in the volume.

I am also indebted to Roderick Peattie, and to the others in the editorial staff of the Vanguard Press. I have never had more cordial assistance and I admire their patience. This is the first book I have ever prepared for the general reader, and at times their patience must have been strained.

Worcester, Massachusetts   W. W. A.

CONTENTS

ILLUSTRATIONS

Acknowledgment: Photographs number 1, 13, 22, 28, 29, and 32 are printed by courtesy of W. W. Atwood; numbers 2, 15, 16, 17, 18, and 21, courtesy of the U. S. Forest Service; number 3, courtesy of the U. S. Department of Mines and Resources; number 4, courtesy of the National Park Service; numbers 5, 8, 24, and title page, courtesy of the National Parks Bureau, Ottawa, Canada; numbers 6, 7, and 23, courtesy of the Canadian Pacific Railway; numbers 9, 12, 14, 19, 27, 30, and 31, courtesy of George Grant; number 10, courtesy of Eugene Kingman; numbers 11 and 25, courtesy of the U. S. Geological Survey; number 20, courtesy of Barnum Brown; number 26, courtesy of the U. S. Department of the Interior.

A PREVIEW OF THE ROCKIES

Understand, I do not hold with the doctrine of the inheritance of acquired characteristics, but, in a manner of speaking, I suppose I have the love of the Rocky Mountains in my blood. My grandfather, an Englishman by birth, and a fervent American by choice, was a great storyteller. Best of all the tales he told were those of a journey by oxcart from St. Joseph, Missouri to Pikes Peak. I can even date the trip: my grandfather, sitting by his campfire, listened to the approaching hoofbeats of an express rider and, as the rider dashed by, shouted, "Who's elected?" The rider shouted back "Lincoln" and thundered into the night. But the great moment of the yarn was when grandfather, all but exhausted from travel, saw high above the quivering haze of the plains a heavenly sign indeed. It was the snowcap of Pikes Peak, the symbol of the goal, one of the most inspiring of the milestones in America's westward trek.

Later, my father and my older brother took the narrow-gauge railway over Marshall Pass, and so to the rough mining camp at Ouray in the San Juans. In my turn I, too, went to

Ouray. In 1910 I stood for hours upon Capital Hill in Denver, studying our greatest panorama, the ever-changing aspect of the distant Rockies. Then I took that most remarkable of railways and crossed Marshall Pass. I found Ouray still little more than a mining camp. It lies at the head of a red-walled canyon where there is always the sound of falling water. As a young geology student, I was not only to map and learn the rocks, but to experience the revelation that comes from one's first alpine peaks. Though in after years I was to know many a mountain, none were more dramatic to me than the San Juans, standing clear and fearless in the desert air.

Yet the most vivid memory of that trip was my meeting with a genuinely distinguished man. He was Wallace W. Atwood, then at the University of Chicago, later at Harvard University, and now President of Clark University and director of a graduate school of geography. I do not know how much the Rockies were responsible for the mental stature and breadth of vision of the man, but I like to think their influence was great. I learned far more from Wallace Atwood on that trip than I did in his classroom. And now, years later, as editor, I have asked my teacher to write the Rocky Mountain volume in the American Mountain Series. In this opportunity I have partly repaid my debt to him, for I find it is the book he has always dreamed of writing.

For more than a score of years Dr. Atwood has studied the Rockies, studied them and loved them. He has ridden with pack train the length of the sky-line trail. Few can boast of having done that. It is America's most thrilling experience. In 1909, the United States Geological Survey sent him into the Rocky Mountains to make a model physiographic study of mountain erosion and sculpture. His various assignments have led him from one range to another, from Colorado and New Mexico to Alaska. Few geologists have remained so faithful to a single problem. Here it was that Dr. Atwood's scientific reputation was established.

More than that, the beauty and drama of the mountains did something to the man. He rode the dangerous mountain trails like a cowboy. His skill and knowledge of mountain ways made him an acknowledged leader of the long pack trains needed to explore the mountain wilderness. Never overlooking the splendor of the mountains, he saw in the rocks, in the lonely cirques at the head of the gorges, in the common levels of the mountains, the intimate story of mountain sculpture. It is an epic story, and he is the one man in the country to tell it completely. For the tale of the Rockies is not the history of men. The mark of man is insignificant on these ranges. The history of the Rocky Mountains is written in the stone itself.

The Rocky Mountains are the eastern, or front, range of the western cordillera. They extend from New Mexico to Canada, to Alaska, where they back the arctic plain. A most important feature of these mighty mountains is their prodigious length. From New Mexico to Alaska, they have a span of thirty-four degrees latitude, or almost one-tenth of the circumference of the world. Whatever the various portions of the Rockies may have in common, the geographer notes that for each latitude a characteristic climate obtains.

Now, the climate of plains country is chiefly told in terms

of distance from the sea and distance from the equator. Mountain climates, however, call for consideration of a third dimension, that of altitude. In the Rockies, running, as they do, parallel to the seacoast and athwart the prevailing westerly winds, distance from the sea corresponds in effect to exposure to the sea winds. Generally speaking, the coast slopes will have more rain and snow than the east exposures. True, by the time the winds have crossed the more western ranges and passed over a thousand miles of almost waterless lands, they have little moisture content. But as they are forced to rise over the great alpine range, attaining colder altitudes, rain and snow occur. If the windward exposure thus has precipitation, the east side, on the contrary, is relatively dry— dry because descending air is being warmed. To cause precipitation, air must be chilled below the saturation point. In so far as the Pacific Ocean is the source of moisture, the east slopes are the drier, and indeed there is a rain shadow (dry strip) that extends theoretically over the plain for a width sixteen times the height of the mountain range.

This does not mean that it does not rain on the east slope. There are eastern sources of moisture and, in any case, mountain winds are capricious. There are, in valleys, many local updrafts which may cause rain. I remember once in a Rocky Mountain valley seeing five distinct thunderstorms, small and not widely spaced, at one time. A comprehensive view of the east front of the mountains may even show half a dozen separate storms simultaneously on a warm summer afternoon.

The eastern winds, which often cause general storms on the drier side of the range, may come from cyclonic storms where the center of the storm lies to the west of the range. These are more evident in winter than in summer.

The question of distance from the equator, or latitude, is most important in the Rockies, for no world range, other than the Andes, lies across more degrees of latitude. And not even the Andes furnish more dramatically contrasting climates, deriving from position. The Rockies stretch from the hot deserts of New Mexico and Colorado, through zones of aridity of a continental interior, through the forest zone of the subarctic, to a bleak snow desert of the true arctic.

But it is the third dimension, that of altitude, that is most astounding and brings up the most numerous questions. Here for the plainsman lies the unfamiliar. Here are conditions which should be understood by the tenderfoot before he ventures on expeditions. Since this is the first book of the American Mountain Series to deal with truly high mountains, your editor takes space to answer a few questions and issue a few warnings.

The first of the altitudinal modifications of climate is brought quickly and uncomfortably to the mountain climber's attention. This is a combination of decreasing oxygen and increasing rarity of air as he ascends. Invigorated by the fresh mountain morning, the untutored climber attacks the ascent of the mountain with energy. He outstrips his guide along the trail. This is a mistake. The slow, measured stride of the guide is best. The enthusiast soon finds himself breathing hard, his heart palpitating, and his legs taking on the weight of lead. How much exhaustion is due to the failure of oxygen in upper levels, and how much is due to low pressures, one

21

cannot say. The fact remains that every hundred feet of ascent brings a significant decrease of oxygen and air pressure. An altimeter for recording heights is really a barometer graduated to feet. Every ten-foot change of elevation can be read on the altimeter, and almost as small a measure is felt by the heart.

The secret of a successful high climb is to take the trail with a slow, steady step. Rest frequently; the higher the altitude, the more frequent the rest. Never take a shortcut up a steep slope. Such cutoffs are for coming down. The longer way up is the less exhausting. Also, if you come from sea level to, say, the base of Pikes Peak, you should loiter about the base of the mountain for several days before undertaking a serious climb. Overstrain may mean palpitation of the heart, trembling of the knees (no good on dangerous slopes), nosebleed, general exhaustion, and even mountain sickness. Mountain sickness is a form of nausea. We are not sure of its cause. Its prevention is good food and gradual change of altitude. Its cure is long rest or, better, to go downslope.

One of the sensible ways to undertake a long trip to a peak is to do as much of the trail on horseback as possible. But remember that the horse feels the altitude also and should be given consideration. If the horse is to be taken to quite high altitudes, the rider may lead him part of the time. If you have a pack train, hang on to the tail of the horse before you. It gives that extra lift you need and does not fatigue the horse. (A long tail puts you safely beyond his hoofs; besides, a horse is not likely to kick on a steep slope.) Often the horse trail leads only to the valley head below the peak. Here in the grassy cirque the horse may be tied or hobbled, and the final ascent over the rocks made on foot.

One of the delights and dangers of high-altitude climbing is the degree of insolation, or direct heat of the sun. Mountain air has low temperature for a number of reasons: the rarity of the air gives little actual material for absorbing heat; composition of the atmosphere at high levels is not of the more heat-absorbing gases; and there are other more technical reasons. The air at high levels is cold because the air there does not absorb much heat and does not easily retain it.

As a natural consequence, the heat of the sun comes through a thin atmospheric blanket and bears directly upon the rocks. Actually, rocks on the peaks may be too hot to touch. Passing a cliff, you can feel the rock heat radiated, as in passing a locomotive. Yet at night the heat is dispelled rapidly. The cold of the rocks will be felt even through thick blankets. Better sleep at the tree line, and make an early start to see the sunrise from the peak. Also, at the tree line there is less wind, and there is fuel for a fire.

The morning sun, penetrating the cold, thin air is delightful; the body is actually warm, yet tingling with the sensation of freshness. But therein lie the dangers from the slight air density. One risk is sunburn. If a person burns badly, cold cream ought to be used before exposure. But it is snow fields or ice that carry the most serious threat, for there the reflected sun from the white surface gets under your hat and burns your face. Moreover, snow blindness is not uncommon, and if that strikes, you may be unable to see for hours. Dark glasses are essential.

23

There is yet another precaution to be taken. You may be warm in the sun, but pass into the shade of a cliff, and you are quickly cooled. Do not strip off too many garments in climbing. A flannel shirt may be a little too warm in the sun, but will be a protection in the shade. An extra sweater or windbreaker is good. The exposed peak is usually windy and cold. After a struggle many a climber has achieved a summit, only to find it too cold, and so has been forced to go down without having time to enjoy the view. Take a windbreaker. When not in use, you can tie the sleeves around your waist.

All this sounds discouraging and overcautious. Not at all. It merely warns the novice that climatic conditions on mountain peaks should be understood and sensibly met. Mountain climbing and exploring is one of the greatest sports in the world. The serenity and sense of sublimity granted him who gains a fine mountain summit are among life's richest sensations. The freshness of the air, the purity of a drink at a mountain stream, the pleasure of the discovery of a glade or view, the delicious heat of the clear mountain sun, the descent into the cool of the canyon, the down-valley breeze of evening, the husky appetite for coffee and bacon over a sweet-smelling fire—these are all superb experiences, fit only for the gods. The mountain stream sparkles in these canyons, and at night the stars shine through the rustling aspens with brilliance. This is Parnassus.

Dr. Atwood has given us a rare combination of science and impression, the two wisely separated in chapters of their own —the scientific observation and the human reaction. Perhaps

24

never before has the great book of earth fact, the story of the rocks, been so freely translated into the language of the layman. Never before has the life history of a mountain range been put on paper with such lucid simplicity. This volume is a milestone of progress in the popularization of scientific fact.

RODERICK PEATTIE

CHAPTER ONE

CLIMBING TO HIGH PLACES

Mountains challenge men. The greater the height and the more difficult the climb, the keener the challenge. And the peak that has never been scaled, the virgin peak, is the most tempting.

But the jagged summits, projected into the blue of the sky, are not easily conquered. The task may be tremendous, may call for astute planning. From a distance, with the help of field glasses, one selects the slopes where the ascent will be easiest. From our camp at the mountain base we imagine ourselves above the tree line, moving along a hogback crest between two mountain gorges, coming to a ragged cliff where we plan to work cautiously upward in some crack or chimney to a bare rocky bench. From there we know we must scramble higher and higher and find a way over or around a glistening snow field until we reach a final steep ascent of two or three hundred feet. We cannot tell from afar how that last part of the task will be accomplished but we feel sure we shall master all difficulties and shall reach the summit.

Every muscle is keyed for the effort. We begin, through anticipation, to get something of the thrill that comes from exercise in the pure, cool air of the high-mountain area. We look forward to each new adventure, each new obstacle, with a desire to measure our strength and skill, the calmness of our nerves, and our perseverance. Nor is this challenge only for the alpinist or trained rock climber! Every visitor to the mountain parklands is inspired to climb and to experience the satisfaction that can be had only by the conquest of some pinnacle or lofty summit.

> Why climb the mountains? I will tell thee why,
> And, if my fancy jumps not with thy whim,
> What marvel? there is scope beneath the sky
> For things that creep, and fly, and walk, and swim.
> I love the free breath of the broad-wing'd breeze,
> I love the eye's free sweep from craggy rim,
> I love the free bird, poised at lofty ease,
> And the free torrent's far-upsounding hymn;
> I love to leave my littleness behind,
> In the low vale where little cares are great,
> And in the mighty map of things to find
> A sober measure of my scanty state,
> Taught by the vastness of God's pictured plan
> In the big world how small a thing is man.*

But besides the thrill of high conquest, there is the excitement of reading in the rocks and contour of the mountain the history of uplift and erosion that have given this earth mass its character. This volume is devoted not so much to the story

* From the anthology, *The Englishman in the Alps*, edited by Arnold Lunn. Oxford University Press, 1913.

30

of alpinism as to the story of the mountain itself. Chapters represent eras and millenniums. Once understood, the mountain comes to have a personality. The task of unraveling the life history of a mountain or a mountain range is a search for clues to be found in the character of the rocks, the contour of the mountain shoulder, and the form of the valley.

It is not always at the peak that the historical clue is discovered. More often, and more vividly, the slopes may reveal the secret of the geologic history. Yet we should not hesitate to take the time needed to reach the summit, if it is practicable, for our topographer may wish to occupy that lofty place as a station from which he can take numerous shots through his telescopic alidade. This instrument is used for sighting distant peaks and reading angles of elevation or depression relative to the station occupied. These shots on the map, which is mounted on a plane table, when combined with shots taken from other stations, make it possible for him to locate the peaks accurately and to determine their exact elevations above sea level. His work is absolutely essential to our discovery of mountain history.

Yet the high places are important outlook stations for all of us. We gather important data about the rock material immediately about us and, with the aid of field glasses, we are able to locate many distant places where essential information may be obtained. We acquire a good general idea of the structure of the range. We gain a sense of proportion, for from the lofty summits the more important features stand out conspicuously, and the little things in the valley bottoms, regardless of how interesting they are to us, shrink into their

31

appropriate places. And that sense of proportion dwindles our own importance. We are truly in a garden of the gods.

Let us select a high and very interesting but not too difficult climb. Our outfitting station will be the beautifully located city of Ouray, nestled in the San Juan Mountains of south-west Colorado, and our goal, the summit of Uncompahgre, 14,306 feet above sea level, the highest peak in the range, and one of the highest peaks in the United States. This expedition will take at least five days, and, if the weather for climbing is unsatisfactory when we reach the base of the mountain, we may be away two or three days more.

The saddle stock and pack train arrive at our camp early on the day of departure. All is made ready as promptly as possible, and we start southward up the magnificent and vari-colored canyon of the Uncompahgre River. At first our route is along the "million-dollar road," cut at places in the solid rock wall of the canyon. It is the old stagecoach route over the range to Silverton, a mining center on the south side of the San Juan Mountains. After about two miles we turn sharply to the left, leave the highway, climb a steep bank, and enter the gorge of Bear Creek. Here the trail is well built and clear of fallen timber. It is a sidehill trail. On our left the mountain slope rises abruptly. From our saddles we look directly at the base of dark-green spruces and firs that cling to the wall of the little tributary gulch through which we are moving. On our right the rock wall droops off precipitously to the clear stream that is tumbling over boulders and swirling huge rock fragments around as it hurries on to join the larger river.

In certain sections the trail is cut into solid rock and is

32

dangerously narrow, especially for the pack animals. Above our heads rock overhangs, and the outer edge of the trail is the brink of a precipice 200 to 300 feet high. We are not protected by a rock wall or anything that might give even a psychological feeling of safety. You can't help wondering what would happen if the horse misstepped only six inches to the right or were startled by a bee or a snake and suddenly jumped from the narrow bench on which we are traveling. But the horses do not misstep and they are not startled. They take it all in the day's work, moving slowly and continuously, higher and ever higher. We are really climbing out of the canyon of the Uncompahgre and trying to reach the American Flat, where the going will be comparatively easy for several miles.

All seems to be progressing well, and the trail is a bit wider, when we are suddenly ordered to dismount. The packers must inspect all saddles and packs. Front cinches are tightened and back cinches on riding saddles are loosened. The packsaddle cinches and the diamond hitches are all checked. The back breechings on the packsaddles are loosened. Our guide announces that we have reached the rimrock of the canyon and face a very steep pitch ahead, called "Hell's Half Mile." It will be a poor trail and a very hard pull for the horses and mules. He says: "Walk if you wish. Take hold of the tail of your horse and let him help you a little. That's not a bad way to get over this stretch. We'll soon be on top and crossing the Flat."

There are eight in our party, in addition to the packers and cooks. It is just such an expedition as almost anyone

33

would enjoy, and for the younger members of my family in the group it is a matter of high adventure. The boys are determined to stick to their saddles and show that they can ride anywhere a horse can go. The girls, who are a little younger, think it best to walk, but they are quick to adopt the packer's suggestion and take hold of the tail of a saddle horse. That is a wonderful help, almost as good as a ski tow. By pulling just a little, not more than the equivalent of five pounds for the horse, it seems almost like walking on a level trail. The procession has its comic aspect, and one of the boys dismounts, camera in hand, to record his sisters' easy but undignified progress. By this maneuver he loses his horse entirely, for the animal has no choice but to keep in line and climb to the top. The photographer is soon glad to grip a tail himself. At places the horses are forced to jump. They pick their way among angular blocks, make many sharp turns, pause for breath, but in time they succeed in reaching the canyon rim without mishap.

We started at an elevation of about 7,800 feet above sea level in Ouray. We are now at 12,700 feet, at the west margin of a broad, gently rolling surface called the American Flat. The horses have lifted us nearly 5,000 feet, a very respectable climb, covering a good share of a hard day's work. While we stop for a late lunch, the saddles are adjusted, for some of them have slipped back too far to be comfortable either for horse or rider. After dropping down about four hundred feet, we start across a meadowland dotted with numerous little ponds and hillocks. Ice must have passed over this surface, smoothed it off somewhat, and, upon melting, left the loose

34

material that now provides a good soil. We are above the tree line, in the zone of alpine grasses, brilliant with color. Thousands of sheep are grazing on the bright-green meadows, clustered in flocks averaging two thousand or so in number. Each shepherd has a little tent that serves as a home, with a bedding ground for the sheep adjoining, and a trough near by, in which he keeps a supply of salt. And each has one or two good dogs to help him round up his flock and keep watch during the night, when hungry bears, wolves, or coyotes are apt to steal into camp.

Mountain ascents on foot are arduous. Too much of our strength is taken up by the effort of the climb. Too much of our attention is given to the trail, which is safe only if we are aware of our foothold. It is only at the rests or in crossing a grassy parkland that we have time and freedom to take in the beauty about us. Look about you now while we are in our saddles again. To the north, scarcely a mile away, is Wildhorse Peak, a sharp pyramidlike summit that stands 13,271 feet above the sea. In the distance are the Matterhorn, with an elevation of 13,589 feet, and the Wetterhorn at 14,020 feet—peaks vividly reminiscent of scenes in Switzerland. These summits are mantled with snow, whose glistening white makes the sky seem a deeper blue. Each is a challenge. But today we must not turn aside from our purpose, for our goal is a higher and prouder peak.

Across the alpine meadow there is no real path. For the moment our horses and we are freed from anxiety about the trail. There is no need to keep in line and we ride beside each other in easy fashion. Though each may choose his route as he pleases, the leader must know where he is headed and he must keep an eye on the ridge he wishes to strike at the far side of the meadow. Keeping an eye on the trail ahead becomes second nature after one has lived in the high mountains a few seasons.

As we approach the far side of the American Flat, we once more watch for trail markers, pick up our route, and fall into line again, on the lookout for a way through the high-mountain country to the head of the North Fork of Henson Creek. Before us and all about us stretches a magnificent mountain panorama, and thousands of feet below us, we spot the gleam of lovely mountain lakes. The tree line crosses the lower slopes at about 11,000 feet.

It is as if the landscape had been swept by some giant's paintbrush, but we geologists note the colors primarily for their revelation of the mineral character of the mountains. One mountain mass is deep red. Its rock contains pyrite, or fool's gold, which glistens like gold, but is an oxide of iron. Another peak is yellow. When that rock mass was oxidized, water joined in the process and formed limonite, yellow iron ore. Here and there prospectors have dug into the hillside, hoping to locate a mineral vein rich enough to justify staking off a claim.

A few scraggly, wind-blown cedars and courageous junipers cling to hillsides, where they have succeeded in twining their roots about angular rock fragments. They are sturdy specimens struggling for existence against tremendous odds. Much of the year they are buried in snow. The growing season at altitudes of 12,000 to 13,000 feet is less than three

The trick is to get the load balanced.

"Come and get it or I'll throw it out." (In the Holy Cross National Forest.)

Folds in the Canadian Rocky Mountains.

Black Canyon of the Gunnison. A gorge cut by the Gunnison River
following its superposition on the late Tertiary peneplain.

months, and it is only during this period that the trees can build new tissue. They never become full grown; they are dwarfs, twisted and gnarled by the terrific winds that at times cross high-mountain areas.

At about four in the afternoon, after traveling at least fifteen miles by pack train, we drop down a few hundred feet into the valley of Henson Creek, to the tree line, and gratefully we pitch camp, at an elevation of about 11,000 feet, near a little meadow and an ice-cold mountain stream. It is a cold spot for a camp, but we are armed against the chill. The sky is clear. We decide there is no danger of rain or snow and vote against putting up tents. The cook works over an open fire whose smoke ascends in a clear, blue spiral. We scatter about in the forest and select places that look good to us for a night's rest, while the wranglers look after the outfit and the stock. After supper, around a roaring campfire, we review the day's experiences, admit to some saddle sores, and look over our map to see how long a trek we have for the next day, when we expect to reach the base of Uncompahgre. But our session is brief, for the compulsion of sleep soon overwhelms us.

Dawn comes all too soon. Snug in a sleeping bag, everyone tries to shut out the sounds of breakfast in the making and the realization that it means leaving comfort for the presunrise chill. The meadow is still in the shadow of the peaks. But, as day breaks, the camp is astir. Pans rattle, horses stamp, and yawning sighs are heard. By the time one is out of the blankets, horses and pack mules are being saddled, and the wonderful smell of bacon and coffee is abroad. We scurry down to the stream. Those who plan to shave beg a little warm water from the cook, hang a metal mirror on a tree, and get through the chore as quickly as possible. As the first sunbeams come over the rim of surrounding peaks and strike camp, a cry of joy goes up, welcoming the warmth of those early-morning rays. Breakfast is quickly over. It is a stand-up affair for the tenderfeet who have had their first day in the saddle. One of the boys says to his friend, "Touch me somewhere." Then he yells, "Touch me somewhere else," trying to find some spot that does not hurt.

After about two hours of hard work, the outfit is all lashed down on the backs of the pack mules, and we are in our saddles and off on the trail again. This second day on the march leads down the North Fork of Henson Creek to an elevation of about 10,400 feet and then northward up an unnamed tributary, which brings us into a basin located between the Matterhorn Peak and Uncompahgre.

The trail now runs for several miles through a forest, and is not difficult for riders or packs. The scenery is peaceful and subdued. The forest shadows are fresh but cold. We see nothing of the grandeur of the lofty mountain summits that encircled us on the preceding afternoon. Shut in by the forest and by the walls of the canyon through which we are moving, our attention is focused on the features close at hand. The stream hurries on noisily, tumbling and sliding over rock ledges and huge boulders, pausing now and then in a quiet pool, where surely there are rainbow trout in hiding, then cutting into a soft bank of earth, only to turn and dash against a rock cliff. It is a youthful stream, full of vigor, trying to

38

deepen its channel and carry its load of sand and gravel to lower and lower places; ready, if dammed, to provide power for men to use.

The forest is chiefly of spruce and fir. A few birds flit through the sun and shadow; ferns and flowering plants are everywhere, and occasionally small game, such as rabbits, squirrels, foxes, porcupines, and chipmunks, peer from the underbrush and scamper away. Deer and all larger game usually slip out of sight before we can have a really good look at them.

Climbing northward toward the Matterhorn Peak, we pass a number of abandoned mining camps and a small ghost town, such as may be found among many of our western mountains. Here a few of us stop as an old man comes out from one of the cabins and appears to be asking questions. He uses a cane, and we notice that he is blind. He has a pitiful amount of ore that he wants someone to take to Lake City to be traded in for food at one of the stores. Living all by himself, far off in the hills, the last survivor of a camp that was once prosperous, he still has faith in the mines that at one time produced great wealth and stays on after all others have abandoned hope, preferring to work, although blind, rather than accept a home in some public institution. He says he knows the ore of his mine by its weight. It is a silver-lead ore, and he may easily be right.

Will we come in and spend the night? Do we wish to examine any of the old mines? He can guide us through any one of them. It is difficult to refuse this lonesome soul the company he craves and to decline his many invitations. We slip a bill

39

into his hand as we leave. As we remount, someone calls out optimistically to the old man: "Perhaps we will stop in on our way back for another visit. Good-bye!" But he shakes his head sadly, knowing he cannot hold us, and turns back to his solitude.

As we work higher and higher, some of the bold, rugged summits of the San Juans come into view. The Matterhorn is directly ahead of us, and bold, rocky walls tower up on either side. At places the decay of the mountains is clearly evident. Angular fragments are falling from the lofty peaks. We can hear the crash of great blocks of rock and see the cloud of dust that rises along the route of descent.

We can see large rock masses that have just cut deep gouges in the soil at the base of a peak. A boulder twenty feet in diameter lies at the side of the trail, and the scar that it made, perhaps but yesterday, is like the tail of a comet stretching far behind it up the mountain. That block may stay a thousand years where it now lies, before it gets another chance to work its way nearer to sea level.

All mountains at high elevations are crumbling. Mountains have their periods of growth and of decay. If they are high above sea level, the natural forces due to changes in temperature, frost action, and gravitation tend to disrupt the rocks and start them on their way to the sea.

In a pass at the east base of Matterhorn Peak, at an elevation of 12,463 feet, we stop for lunch, which today is a very simple meal. The cook has prepared a sandwich or two for each of us, topped off with graham crackers, a few raisins, and a bar of chocolate as dessert. There is plenty of good mountain water available.

At the luncheon stop we are in full view of the mountain we are to climb. Here is the cliff we studied from our valley camp. Here is our challenge, the mountain face so imposing, so menacing, that merely looking upward to its peak makes us dizzy. The west face of Uncompahgre rises for two thousand feet as a bare rock wall, jagged with formidable cliffs one hundred to two hundred feet high that seem impossible to climb. The upper thousand feet on the west side of the mountain is extremely steep and may never be climbed.

The huge bulk of the mountain is made up of layers of lava that poured forth from some fissure or some volcanic vent. The layers are nearly horizontal and appear to be but a remnant of a plateau of such rocks, which formerly spread over most of the mountain area. The lavas are predominantly of a pinkish color, though some are a deep maroon. Variation in hardness makes the gentler slopes alternate with steep or almost vertical walls. But, for all that, the north face of Uncompahgre is nearly vertical for at least a thousand feet. It is the end wall of a great amphitheatral basin where an alpine glacier formed, and the movement of the ice away from the base steepened that wall. The peak is asymmetrical, sheer on the north and gentle on the south. On the latter slope, where we plan to ascend, some of the climbing will be easy, but some will test our abilities to the utmost.

We camp near a clump of trees in the basin west of Uncompahgre and north of the Matterhorn, choosing the spot with

41

a view to a ready supply of firewood and an enclosure where the packers can make a rope corral for their stock and tie the animals while they are being saddled. Here we put up our small tents and make ourselves camp-comfortable, for we expect to stay two nights and perhaps longer. We have a wonderful outlook, which is especially beautiful and restful during the late afternoon and in the evening, as the sunset glow illuminates the sky, then deepens to purple night. Again in the early morning, the rays of the sun strike the top of our chosen peak, dyeing it crimson, and then creep slowly to lower and lower levels.

Before turning in, orders are issued for the next day. We are at a point between 11,000 and 11,500 feet above sea level. The climb ahead of us is about 3,000 feet, and we plan to ride to the south base of the mountain and up the first few hundred feet, where the slope is rather gentle. There we will leave our horses, in care of one of the packers, to graze on the rich bunch grass of the mountainside until we return late in the afternoon. Everyone must be up promptly for breakfast and dressed for climbing. Hobnailed boots are now in order. Each one will carry his own lunch and a packet of emergency rations. The leader of the party will have a first-aid kit with him. In making our way over the occasional perilously steep places we are admonished to follow the leader and to be particularly careful not to loosen rocks that might fall on someone below. In these dangerous sections no one should become entirely separated from the group. And in all high mountain work no individual should ever make a solo trip, for even a sprained ankle may require the assistance of a companion.

The next day, scheduled for the climb, the weather is ideal. The early-morning sky is perfectly clear, the mountain air cool and invigorating. There is not much wind. We have every reason to believe we can make the summit by noon, remain two or three hours, return to the horses by four, and be back in camp by five. It should be a glorious day in the mountains, and from the summit we should be able to see most of the San Juan Range, a mountain area that has been called "The Switzerland of America."

When we reach the south base of Uncompahgre, we find that even on the lower slopes of the mountain the horses cannot go directly upward. And so we work out a series of long zigzags, but even then we must stop every few minutes to allow the animals to "blow" or get their breath. We are between 12,000 and 13,000 feet above the sea. The air is less dense than the air to which the horses are accustomed. There is no trail, and the footing is not very good.

At the base of a steep pitch, at about 12,500, we dismount and turn our horses over to the packer. In a few minutes everyone is ready to start. But some move off too rapidly, for good mountain climbers should stick to a slow, even pace and make as few stops as possible. With each rise of one or two hundred feet the mountain vista becomes more inspiring. It would be a shame to push on just to reach the summit. A climb of 800 to 1,000 feet an hour is all we need to make, so why not enjoy the outlook?

Our entire climb is over rock materials that are intensely interesting. There are layers of volcanic dust, loosely cemented, and cinders that must have been thrown high and

43

come to rest in this particular place. Someone discovers a spherical form about eight inches in diameter, composed of successive layers or shells of lava. It is a volcanic bomb that was blown upward from a crater. It cooled and then fell into a pool of molten lava, received another layer of lava, and was blown into the air again. This process must have been repeated several times before the bomb fell outside the crater and rolled down the slope of the mountain.

At 13,000 feet we are clambering over huge, angular blocks of lava. A dense, hard layer forms a cliff, and we have some real difficulty in getting over this part. There is no danger of falling off the mountain, but there is no good footing and care must be taken not to slip and fall. The air is becoming very thin, and we all must breathe in more air in order to get the amount of oxygen needed. We inhale deeply, with shoulders thrown well back.

At the top of this climb we have attained 13,300 feet elevation. There are about 1,000 feet of vertical ascent ahead of us, and about one mile to cover in horizontal distance. Very few of the peaks in the range rise higher than the spot at which we have arrived. Hundreds of square miles of peak on peak or gentle slope are spread out before us to the south and southwest. To the southwest we can pick out Rio Grande Pyramid, 13,830 feet. Like Uncompahgre it consists of layers of lava. Some day we must climb that peak! Farther to the southwest are the Needles, the "unclimbable," sheer, dramatic obelisk-like forms, thousands of feet above their surroundings. They are made of the most ancient of rocks, and may be regarded as in the core of the range. To the west, far beyond Ouray, our

44

starting point, is Mt. Sneffels, an exceedingly difficult climb, but interesting, for it is the core of an ancient volcano.

We push on now over steep places, where we almost get down on our hands and knees and crawl over ledges and over some long, gentle slopes. At about 13,400 feet our path upward becomes very narrow, and we find ourselves on a ridge, or saddle, at the very rim of the nearly vertical west wall of the mountain. A misstep to the left would mean a tragedy. We are ordered into single file and warned to attend strictly to the work of climbing the next few hundred yards. The dangerous narrows passed, we begin the last and most difficult and tiring part of the climb. The thinness of the air is affecting all of us, but fortunately, no one is sick nor complains of being dizzy nor of any pains about the heart. We can all stand the exertion at this altitude, but we move ever more slowly.

The last pull over the rim of the summit platform is the hardest. Once past this obstacle, we shall easily mount to the highest part of the mountain. Heated by exertion and suddenly exposed to chilling winds, the sweaters, coats, and windbreakers now serve their purpose. The moment of achieving the summit is the moment of a great physical victory; one is almost inclined to shout news of conquest to an unhearing world. But it is not the physical victory that matters; it is the view from a great mountain peak that rewards us with an indescribable spiritual experience. Climbers seek lonely vantage points where they may study the confusion of peaks and the valley lands spotted with moving cloud shadows and from the beauty of the scene discover soul-satisfaction such as they never had known before. Some of the most beautiful passages in English literature have been written on viewing the world from a mountain peak. . . . Silence settles over our party, and there is a universal desire to be alone. You shun noisy companions as you do when in a beautiful cathedral. There are always those who try to capture beauty with a camera. But better yet, let the scene before you soak in so that it may later be recalled by that "inward eye that is the bliss of solitude."

In exploring the summit of Uncompahgre, we discover that the men of our national surveys have occupied this summit. A metal bench mark, carrying the elevation of the summit, is cemented into a large mass of rock at the highest point. Here the surveyors placed telescopic instruments and sighted distant peaks. Some of these men were members of the Coast and Geodetic Survey, who were locating a series of elevations from the Atlantic to the Pacific Oceans. They were noting on their map the exact positions of conspicuous features in the landscape and were determining elevations. Another group occupying this mountain top as an outlook station was engaged in making the local topographic map we are using. They worked in detail on the features that could be seen to great advantage from this station. From here, someone with the skill of an artist sketched in the contour lines of each mountain, each valley, each basin, each mountain spur within sight, indicating drainage features, lake locations, and the extent of forested areas.

The United States surveyors selected Uncompahgre for many of the same reasons that tempted us to choose this peak.

46

The outlook from the summit is superb. Below us are huge amphitheatral, or cirquelike, basins which we look into from aloft. Bounded by nearly vertical rock walls, these basins have numerous lakes scattered about on their floors, and great heaps of glacial debris. These are the places where the accumulated snows formed the ancient alpine glaciers of this section of the range. Seventy glistening lakes are visible from the top of this mountain, lying high in the range, jewels in the landscape. They have particularly beautiful shades of blue or green because of the reflection of light or algae living in the waters.

In a northerly direction from the summit of Uncompahgre, the volcanic rocks are highly colored, like those in the canyon of the Yellowstone. They all contain iron, and in the weathering or disintegration in the presence of water the decayed rocks take on various tones of yellow, brown, and red. The panorama is a challenge to a painter or to anyone interested in color photography.

For fifty miles in almost every direction we look upon a vast sea of mountain peaks, into deep canyons, across plateau-like summit areas, over glittering snow fields, brightly colored meadows, and dark forested areas.

Mining camps scattered about on the mountains tell a tale of the hopes and ambitions of men slaving to make fortunes. Shepherds in the distance are guarding their sheep and counting the days until fall, when they can return to village or ranch life. Some of the valleys are dotted with houses, minute to our eyes, yet bearing the stamp and spell of home for some little family of mountain dwellers. Far off a train must be

47

moving through a distant canyon, for a column of smoke travels slowly along the horizon.

But though we are above all this, isolated and free from care, we are not unmindful of the history behind this world. All about us in the rocks, in the mountain forms, in the sky, the pastures, forests, and mineral wealth in the rocks, there are reminders of changes that have taken place during those eons that have made the territory habitable for men. There must be some deeper meaning to all this. We shall return to regions where men cluster in dense settlements obscuring the old earth story, and we should have a better perspective on human affairs.

The clouds that were beginning to form when we reached the summit became larger and larger. By two o'clock great masses of warm air soaring from the valleys are cooling to the dew point at an elevation of about 13,000 feet. At that level the vapor rising in the air changes into tiny globules of water, uniting as they float upward to form rolling white clouds.

Soon we look down on a billowy surface of pure white, in which the cloud masses are constantly rolling over and over, like waves of a restless sea. Banks of cloud rise hundreds of feet and then drift away, to be lost in the great white foam. Windows open here and there, and for a brief moment give us glimpses of the vivid mountain landscape. Thin, fleecy clouds spread delicate veils over forests, lakes, and alpine meadows.

Watching these constantly changing scenes, time has been forgotten, but the signal to descend breaks our mood of spiritual exultation. One last look over the circle of the horizon. Is it possible that in this chaos of peaks about us we stand on the highest point? Below us lies the world of nature, and the struggle nature implies. Down in the valleys men plan and toil and concern themselves with insignificant schemes. For an hour we have been above the petty details of human existence. We have been fed upon heavenly beauty. It is with a shock that we are brought to the realization that we are only human beings with ordinary responsibility. We must return to earth. Reluctantly we begin the descent.

CHAPTER TWO

OPENING A FIELD SEASON

Al's voice rings out, "Come here, you wild cayuse! You've had three days off. Well, you'll have a double load for this. I'll show you how to act in a corral. Put on a blindfold, Pete, while we cinch this devil up and put on a pack that will let him know he has a day's work to do." Al's bright neckscarf flutters in the breeze, and he spits vehemently. "You know, this animal has no kindness in him. I've treated him gently all my life and been mighty good to him, but he's a devil. The better I treat him, the meaner he gets. Look out for his heels there, young fellow; he's likely to lift you into the air and, if he did, you'd be on the other side of that mountain when you landed."

Slowly the echoes from the corral die out. Each of the animals stands patiently awaiting his share of the camp equipment or his particular rider. Beds are being rolled up, tents folded, the stove is cooling off, panniers are being loaded and carefully weighed.

All this is part of Al's job. He is head packer and a very

53

important man. It is his responsibility to see that the sidepacks for each animal are of equal weight, that all the articles of equipment are in their right places, and particularly, that the scientific instruments are put where the animals will not roll over on them.

If you like mountains, and men, and even mules, you will enjoy Al and his stories; you will also enjoy learning of the making of mountains, of the many vast changes that have taken place in this area over millions of years and, finally, of the coming of miners, ranchmen, and lovers of the outdoor world. We invite you to join us in camp, sit down with us at campfire conferences, and ride in a saddle with a pack train through the mountains.

We are about to leave our first base camp and start off for another field season in some of the roughest and highest country in Colorado. There we will carry forward a work that should lead, after years of such study, to an understanding of the formation, growth, decay, rejuvenation, and glaciation of the Rocky Mountains. We are dealing with periods of history that precede by millions of years the coming of man into this part of the world, yet, at the same time, we are dealing with processes active today. They lead us to understand intelligently the physical features and the natural resources where men have discovered fabulous mineral wealth, magnificent forests, rich pasture lands and many places of such outstanding scientific interest, scenic beauty, and inspirational value that they have been set aside as national reservations.

Plans for taking to the field for a season in the high mountains as a geologist of the United States Geological Survey must be made long before summer arrives. Maps must be selected, photographically enlarged, sectioned, and mounted so as to fold into a convenient size. The published maps are usually on the scale of one-half inch, or one inch, to the mile. In order to record our field observations we need a map scaled to two or three inches to the mile.

We engage camp helpers, requisition our instruments, purchase photographic supplies, prepare lists of provisions, and, just before leaving home for the field, we order the reshoeing of the horses and mules, which have been wintering at a ranch near the mountains.

Upon our arrival in the West, we check over the camp equipment, and see that all necessary repairs are made. Sometimes we need another saddle horse or pack animal. Finally, we purchase provisions, each man mails a jubilant letter to someone saying that we are off to the wilds, and we turn to the final job of packing.

A FIELD PARTY

Until rather recent years, extensive field studies in any part of the Rocky Mountains required the organization and equipment of a pack train, the selection of saddle horses suitable for trail work, the purchase of a camp outfit appropriate for use in high mountain areas, and the enlistment of at least one packer and one cook. Today it is possible to work certain sections of the mountain area with a small car, and tomorrow the helicopter will prove to be wonderfully helpful in high mountain studies. But a pack-train expedition is sure to provide more interesting adventures and bring you into a more intimate association with the mountains than any of the modern means of more rapid travel. It is a mistake to go through or over the mountains too rapidly.

There should always be at least two scientific workers in a surveying party assigned to a high-mountain region, and it is more economical and efficient to have at least four on the technical staff. If you increase the party beyond six, the packer will want an assistant, and the cook may also call loudly for a helper. Then you may as well go to ten or twelve in the party, if you can find assistants who have been properly trained and who are physically and temperamentally well equipped for hard work, some rough going, and absence for months from "Main Street." It will be a simple life of crude comfort, but one full of inspiration and excitement for the lovers of the great world where there are no windows except those torn in clouds and no doors to shut on the wilderness.

If we plan for a party of four men, we must have one pack animal for the personal equipment of each two men, and four for the cook and general camp equipment. That will make a pack train of six, not too many for one man to take care of on the trail. We will all help in the daily packing and unpacking and also in any emergency if trouble comes. There must be four saddle horses, though it will be fortunate if we can have at least one more, for it is almost too much for a saddle horse to work six days out of seven at carrying a rider over high mountain trails, often forcing a route over rough country where there is no trail. Even one extra saddle horse will make it possible to allow each one in the string a day off occasionally.

Many a time I have ridden a pack mule for a day in order to give my saddle horse a rest. A man can stand the strain, but most horses cannot.

Necessary equipment for the pack train and riding animals will include saddles, bridles, saddle blankets, tie ropes, sling ropes, lash ropes, hobbles, bells, a shoeing outfit with an extra set of shoes for each animal, nose bags, grain, panniers, and mantas. The cook will demand a table, a stove or some Dutch ovens, cooking utensils, and dishes, knives, forks, and spoons of various kinds, two pails, a large dishpan, and at least two axes. There must be at least three tents. Each two men should have a sleeping tent, and the cook can get along with one tent in which to cook, store provisions, and serve the meals. That tent should be eight feet by ten, with three-foot walls. In good weather the meals, as a rule, are eaten outdoors.

For provisions we plan to start off with a reasonable supply of essentials: flour, baking powder, corn meal, butter, lard, cocoa, coffee, evaporated milk or cream, eggs, bacon, ham, potatoes, onions, lima and navy beans, cereals, raisins, prunes, dried apples and apricots, canned fruits and vegetables, cheese, jam, marmalade, and dot chocolate. We will pick up a little fresh fruit and meat just as we leave town. After we get away from civilization, we can count on plenty of trout and some game. Occasionally we may make a deal with a shepherd and get some fresh mutton. And if we have a really good cook, he will take a little yeast into camp and fix a pail of sour dough, so that we can have raised bread most of the time. Baking-powder biscuits are all right when they are fresh and hot, but they are not much good when cold. Our noonday lunch, when

57

we are off at work, is the hardest meal to plan. Ham, cheese, bacon, egg, or jam sandwiches go very well if made with good bread, and a piece of dot chocolate tops it off. Of course, we always have plenty of cold clear mountain water and we stop several times during the day for a deep, refreshing drink at a stream crossing or spring. As the season advances, we search for wild berries at lunch time and eat them, sun-warmed.

THE PACK TRAIN

The character of the horses and mules selected for the pack train is of utmost importance. Most pack animals are interesting creatures. I remember one that always wanted to be in the lead on a trail, for she liked to set the pace. Another would go regularly to the cook tent after each meal for the garbage. One year in camp, we had a very canny little mule that seemed to know when moving day was coming, for on such occasions she would wander away from the other animals very early in the morning and hide. This caused us plenty of trouble and delay. She wasn't far away, but in some thick brush and standing perfectly still. She didn't want to be left behind, but she didn't want to carry a pack. If we started without her, she would follow at a safe distance. The packer was not afraid of losing her for she was fond of the other animals and she had always been a pet at the ranch where she was raised. A strong, well-trained mule that will willingly carry a load of 150 to 200 pounds is a treasure. Such an animal may be entrusted with cameras, surveying instruments, and even with fresh eggs. For some animals we reserve the bedrolls, for they can stand a good many hard knocks on the trail.

The first time that we pack an outfit always proves to be the hardest. We must plan to have the side packs for each animal of equal weight. A difference of just a few pounds will raise havoc. The saddle is sure to loosen a little during the day as the animal uses up his strength and, if it becomes too loose, the load will turn. That frightens most animals, and they begin to kick and buck. If the provisions or scientific instruments make up the pack, it is certainly too bad. If it is a load of bedrolls and tents, no great harm is done, but then there is the delay and the work of repacking.

Tent poles adapted to a pack-train trip are all jointed. The cookstove and dining table are collapsible and fit conveniently into the packs. No bundle or article of equipment, when ready for the pack, should be over three and one-half feet long. Generally, the top packs are tents, pails, and dishpan, which, because of their large size are usually tied on last. That is a bad place for them to be if the pack animal should accidentally roll down the mountainside, although most packers take this chance. If we are to travel through a forest, it is well to have the axes carried, so that we can get at them quickly. We may come to down timber that must be cut away.

The trail laid out by the leader of the party should be followed by the packs, but now and then it is necessary for an animal to step aside a little so that a side pack does not hit a tree. Each step on a steep sidehill must be taken with care, and the fording of a swift stream with a bouldery bed demands

59

extraordinary patience. The sure-footedness of a mule is invaluable in trail work. I have seen many a pack animal misstep on a hillside, lose balance, and roll over one, two, or three times. As yet, I have never lost an animal that way. A huge pack will protect the body, and, if the animal's head does not strike a rock, he comes through such an experience without being hurt badly. When an animal rolls down the hillside, we run to the rescue, take off the load, remove the saddle, examine head, back, and legs, and walk the creature around a little before repacking. If all is well, we are soon on the trail again.

I remember one instance where a rolling pack animal, from high on a zigzag trail, was headed straight for a mounted saddle horse on a lower switchback. We had a bad moment. Watchful Al was out of his saddle in a flash, his revolver leveled, ready to shoot the rolling animal, if it seemed necessary, to avoid a collision with one of the party. Two animals and rider rolling down a steep mountainside together might have caused a fatal accident. As it happened, the rider who was in danger pulled up his horse, kept him out of the way, and the pack animal crossed the lower trail and went on caroming downhill a little farther, squealing and pawing the earth before coming to a stop.

A bad pack animal is a terrible problem. He may refuse to stand while the pack is being put into place and may, at any moment, begin to buck the load off. I have seen cereals, hams, bacon, eggs, condensed milk, sugar, flour, and camp dishes go shooting in all directions and spilling down the hill because some pack animal misbehaved. On occasions like that, the air is usually blue, and not with smoke. Every such experience makes the problem of using that animal more trying. Pack mules seem to be repeaters. They like to do the same thing over and over again. Some "packs" will not follow a trail, or they will stop to graze or run off and, carelessly or intentionally, bang a side pack against a tree and knock it out of place. Then kicking begins, the pack turns, a cinch strap breaks, and we are in for another wearying job. If this happens during a heavy rain, or near the end of a day when everyone is tired, it takes some courage, a strong will power, and a sense of humor to get everything, including tempers, together again and be ready to move on to the next camping place.

Some packers never allow the animals any freedom on the trail. They tie one to another and line them up in single file. Each packer then takes the lead rope of the first animal in the string of five or six packs and gets into his own saddle. This method is all right if the trail is not too difficult, but when there are very steep places, swift streams, bogs, or very bad footing for any other reason, the animals should be given their freedom and plenty of time. Patience is a good quality for a packer at work in the mountains.

In packing an animal for a mountain trail, special attention should be given to placing the saddle blankets on without any wrinkles. The animal's back must be treated with great care at all times for a pack animal with a sore back is almost useless. Second, the saddle must be put on correctly, all straps adjusted, and the saddle cinched reasonably tight. Then let the animal walk about or stand for a while and, just before throwing the packs into place, cinch the saddle good and tight to the

61

animal's back. It is a kindness to the beast to keep the saddle well cinched and snug. As the day proceeds it may be necessary to tighten the cinches again, for a packsaddle must not come loose.

Sling ropes hold the side packs in place. A top pack, usually a tent, may be added, and then a large piece of canvas, called a manta, is used to cover and protect the entire load. Now we are ready for the long lash rope and a diamond hitch. The art of throwing that hitch commands the highest respect among western packers, and there is nothing that will put an easterner or the scientific leader of an expedition in such good grace with the camp helpers as putting on a diamond hitch properly.

The lash rope, twenty-five to thirty feet long, must tighten up each side pack and pull the top pack down snugly. This must be done without using a knot, and at the end of the task a loop must be made that will hold all day, and yet be easily loosened at night by a jerk on the end of the rope. If we travel through rain, the ropes will shrink and a bad knot is an ugly thing to find when everyone is trying to make camp in a hurry. If such a knot is found in a lash rope, strong language is almost sure to be heard and deserved. The diamond that gives the name to the hitch is on top of the pack and should open up in good form just as the job is completed.

The work on moving days is always so strenuous and takes so much time away from the scientific studies that we try to plan our trip so that camp may remain at least a week in one place. This means that there will be about twelve moving days in the average field season in a high mountain region. On the other days the packers and cook usually have considerable leisure. There may be repair work to be done on the saddles, or two or three shoes to be put on, and the cook may have some baking to do, but the camp men generally find plenty of time to fish and hunt. One season we had a packer who made each member of the party a pair of leather chaps. We provided him with good materials and all the tools he needed. He was very skillful in leatherwork and, as the season advanced, one after another of the men received his pair of those long leather coverings, buckled them around his waist, adjusted each snap, and mounted his horse as proudly as a typical dude camper. I still have my pair. They provide wonderful protection when riding through a scrub-oak forest or in a heavy rain. Some men wear them most of the time while in the saddle, but they are rather warm and heavy. They are no good when tramping or climbing on foot.

OUR FIELD PLAN

All summer we live as nomads. Weeks pass when we see no one but the members of our party. The life of a fieldworker is one of continuous physical activity, and calls for very strenuous exertion. Though the time in a saddle may be restful and even exhilarating, we stop at frequent intervals when some outcrop of rock must be examined, a hill or mountain crest must be scaled, or we must descend into some gulch in order to get at the formations we are studying. Many a time, when we wish to leave our saddle horses, we throw the reins—which are always left open—over their heads and allow them to drag on the ground. The horses will graze with the reins down, but, if well broken, they will not wander far away. An hour or two may pass before we are ready to remount.

Unless our physical activity is accompanied by intellectual stimulus, no results worth having will be secured; our scientific problems will remain unsolved; and the entire investment of funds, time, and effort will be of little avail. Therefore, the entire experience, physical and intellectual, should be strenuous.

Once camp has been established, the fieldworkers plan to go into different sections of the near-by area each day, and before moving day comes around again they should have visited all places of significance within a day's ride. On rainy days and Sundays we remain in camp, work up our maps, compile data, complete notes, write letters, work up our accounts, and loaf. While at work for the United States Geological Survey, we must send all accounts and salary vouchers to Washington once a month.

If long side trips from a headquarters camp must be made and an overnight stop is necessary, two men go together and lead a pack animal on which a light camp outfit has been placed. These are "fly camp trips" to out-of-the-way places, or to the very high parts of the range. Such little expeditions are fun and often full of thrills and the best of fellowship. The two men must do everything for themselves. Most of the time they must find their way to their objectives without trails, carry through their scientific study and mapping, select a camping place and do all the packing, unpacking, hobbling of stock, putting up camp, cooking, dishwashing, and possibly the shoeing of a horse. If one of the animals throws a shoe, he must

64

not be allowed to go barefoot. A good shoeing kit should be part of every outfit. The men on "fly camp trip" learn to depend entirely upon themselves.

Day after day and week after week, our healthy, hardy camp life continues. But days and weeks are not counted. Never is life monotonous. And moreover, one's physical well-being makes the season seem all too short. Camps are moved from time to time, and each new site offers new excitement. Each day brings in fresh material by which one pieces out the story of the mountain. The fresh, clear air, pure water, simple food, with plenty of mountain trout and game, the wholesome exercise, the beauty of the forest and alpine gardens, the grandeur of the mountain peaks—all these combine to make the life invigorating and delightful. The end of each field season comes too soon.

Sometime between the fifteenth and the twenty-fifth of September the field season in the wilderness areas high among the Rockies must come to a close. This is the time of year when ice forms overnight if water is left in any of the camp dishes. The little lake where we like to take our morning plunge is frozen over. Almost any day or night a soft, fluffy blanket of snow-white flakes may mantle the entire landscape, burying whatever was left out around the camp and covering the pastureland where we'd expected the stock to feed overnight. The animals are almost certain to wander off if the grass is buried under snow and so it is time we were on our way.

While in camp high in the San Juan Range of southwestern Colorado, I remember waking one morning to find what had been a brilliant autumn landscape the day before transformed into one of midwinter. The snow had come so quietly that no one in camp had been disturbed. The cook had forgotten where he left his ax, and the problem of starting a campfire perplexed him. Some of the men had left their heavy woolen socks near the dying embers of the evening fire. Audible exclamations resounded through camp as the men, barefoot, hunted for their socks under the snow. One man had left his heavy shoes beside the fire, hoping they would be dry and warm in the morning. They were buried. Fortunately, the packer had assembled all the saddles, both for the riding horses and for the pack mules, and had thrown over the pile one of the heavy canvas mantas used in covering an animal's pack while on the trail. But the entire string of camp animals had left us!

We had a little grain in camp, which we poured into nose bags, and two of us set out to find the indispensable animals. Fortunately, we knew the footprints of each horse and mule, for we had shod them during the season and had trailed them many times before. After about four hours, we came upon the entire outfit grazing peacefully on a mountain slope where very little snow had fallen. They all knew us, for we had lived together for many weeks. Each man picked out a good saddle horse that he could walk up to with a nose bag clearly visible. Each captured his animal, made a rope bridle, and mounted bareback. After that, there was little trouble in herding the rest of the bunch back to camp.

After breakfast we went searching for odds and ends about the camp, brought together everything we had found, packed up, and hit the trail for the low country. There was no use in

66

staying longer. The trails were covered with snow, and the footing was uncertain. Our desire to get as much work done as possible had led us to stay too long.

The task of descending the mountain slopes was not an easy one, but, as we were all old-timers, we succeeded by the end of the day in getting below the snow line and establishing a new camp in a spot that offered grass for our horses and mules, and dry places where we could set up our tents. The stop was necessary, for we had to reassemble our outfit and take stock of what we had saved and what had been lost. Each succeeding day we pushed on to still lower country, and we came in time to the belt of ranch houses.

About the last thing to do in closing up field work is to locate a ranchman who will take care of the stock during the eight or nine months between field seasons. We want a good pasture and a responsible man who will not work the animals for his own gain and will not allow them to wander away. He is well paid for pasturing and caring for the stock. Before leaving his place, we see that all shoes are taken off, to allow the animals to run unshod during the fall and winter seasons, so that in the spring we shall find their feet in good condition. This is a matter of great importance with mountain horses. A horse for high-altitude trail work is worth no more than his feet.

The camp equipment must be stored also, and, since there are many woolen blankets used under the packsaddles and a large amount of leather in the outfit, we must find a place free both from moths and ever-busy rats. Some ranchmen are not sufficiently reliable to be entrusted with our outfit of pack and

67

riding saddles, bridles, and blankets, so sometimes the camp equipment must be taken to a town, where storage space in some partially vacant building is rented.

Then we say good-bye to the camp hands, pack our personal belongings, and, with bundles of notebooks, maps, and instruments, we take the first through train for home.

OUR OBJECTIVE

Little by little, as one field season follows another, each member in the scientific staff of the party gathers more and more detail of structure of the hard rock formations, the distribution of gravels, glacial debris, and all other varieties of loose or fragmental material. The forms or contours of the lands come to have great significance. As the work proceeds, our maps carry in different colors a welter of notes, which are the basis of the plot of the mountain story.

Gradually we work out the history of the origin and growth of one range after another. The birth of the mountains must be fixed in geologic time; the amount and nature of the uplift determined. Periods of volcanic activity may have occurred: long eras when rock disintegration and the carving of the mountain mass by streams have passed into history; the renewal of mountain growth may have come about; the huge modern canyons are excavated; amphitheatral basins or glacial cirques are developed at the heads of valleys; waterfalls, benches, broad, open valleys, and meadowlands come into the story; the burial of some mountains has taken place, and others are resurrected.

68

Mt. Rundle, Banff National Park, Alberta. In this mountain the sedimentary layers are upturning at high angle. They are part of a huge fold which has been faulted and dissected.

The town of Banff and a great mountain fold to the north. Banff, in the midst of a forest in the valley of the Bow River, is headquarters for many an expedition setting forth to explore the wonders of the Canadian Rockies.

Lake Louise. In the skyline, at the right, is Victoria Mountain, and on its slopes rests Victoria Glacier, which formerly pushed far down the valley beyond Lake Louise and there left a morainic mass which blocks drainage and makes possible this beautifully located body of water.

The mountain panorama south of Lake Louise. From left to right, Mt. Aberdeen, Mitre, Mitre Pass, Lefroy, Abbott's Pass, and a part of Mt. Victoria, Banff National Park, Alberta, Canada. At the lower right is a glacier strewn and at places completely covered with morainic debris.

Little by little the late physical history of the entire mountain province, involving at least sixty million years, is unraveled. We can now tell that story in such terms that anyone who wishes can understand what has transpired in the evolution of the mighty relief features of the Rocky Mountains, which add so much of beauty and grandeur to our western landscape.

Rich deposits of gold, silver, copper, lead, zinc, and many other minerals have accumulated in these mountain ranges. They were once deep below the surface, but stream erosion and glaciation have uncovered them at many localities. Coal was formed at places, and, near the foothills of some of the ranges, petroleum has become concentrated in certain of the rock strata. These natural resources have played an important part in the economic development of the United States and Canada.

Ten to twenty-five thousand years may have passed since various groups of primitive tribesmen began to migrate from northeastern Asia, by way of the Aleutian Islands and Alaska, into the lands of North America. So far as is known, they were the first representatives of the human race to make their homes on this continent. They spread slowly southward and came in time to live in the foothill belts and parklike meadowlands of the cordilleran portions of the United States and Canada. Many of their descendants still live in the area of our field studies, and we shall report later some of our experiences with them. Others of the Stone Age period migrated eastward and southeastward over the interior plains and older mountains of the east and were present near the Atlantic seaboard to welcome the first of the Europeans who came to the Western World. Certain groups of these earliest of American people moved slowly southward into Mexico, Central America, and even to the Andean regions of Peru and Bolivia. There they developed the remarkable civilizations, of olden days, of the Aztecs, Mayans, and Incas.

A few hundred years ago white men came into this mountain region with a spirit of adventure. The first were trappers seeking the beautiful furs of the wild animals of the mountain area. Then came the picturesque prospectors of yesterday. They trudged over the great mountain slopes and through the valleys, usually with a little burro as burden bearer and companion, searching for mineral veins or rich placer deposits. Where these ever-hopeful treasure seekers were successful, mining camps were established, mining towns grew up, and when the ores were worked out, the towns were deserted. They are the "ghost towns" of the mountains today.

Ranchmen came into the Rocky Mountain area and brought flocks of sheep and herds of cattle. Some brought goats, others brought horses, and the pasturelands of the mountains came into regular and systematic use. The valley bottoms are now occupied by the ranchmen as homes and as the wintering grounds for the sheep and cattle, which are driven into the alpine pastures for the summer seasons. Transhumance, the seasonal migration of flocks and herds from plain to mountain alp, became established, and the modern pastoral life in the mountains came to resemble that in mountain regions of much older settlements in the ancient world.

About the margins of the mountains industrial cities sprang

up. Smelting centers were established, where the ores could be treated and metals made available for manufacturers. Railroad engineers laid out zigzag or long, curving routes that locomotives could follow in pulling freight and passenger trains over the mountain, puncturing the rocky walls with holes and tunnels drilled and blasted through their cores, to avoid the long grades necessary in crossing on the surface. High among the mountains, resort hotels and summer camps reared hospitable roofs. Magnificent automobile roads were constructed, national parks set aside, national forests established, and ski trails selected. In time, we have the modern complex picture of man's utilization of these regions of inspiring landscape.

As the story of the Rockies unfolds, keep in mind that much of the time, while our work is in progress, we are in the saddle, following trails through the valleys or along the sky lines of the mountains. Everywhere we go, during twenty-five field seasons, we gather significant data that must all be woven together in order to tell you the story recorded in the following pages.

So the story runs for the Wind River Range, the Big Horns, the Lewis and Clark Ranges, and a score of other Rocky Mountain areas, where the records of the ancient glaciers will unfold.

CHAPTER THREE

THE
MOUNTAIN DRAMA UNFOLDS

How does one learn to read the mountain's story? Chiefly, the geologist, almost like a detective, finds his clue in what is known as structure; that is, in the layering of the rocks and their subsequent deformation. The granite core of the Rocky Mountains is without layers. It has no internal structure that marks it off in beds. But the foothills are made of shales, sandstones, and limestones, of sediments laid down in the sea. These sedimentaries have been bent upward by the thrust of the granite from the interior of the earth. It is in these upturned rock beds that we find our first chapter of the mountain history. The length of the eastern margin of the Rockies has this sedimentary foothill zone. Though not as prominent, there are similar upturned beds on the western margin of the granite core.

These rocks, east and west, can be identified as the same layers by their physical character and by the fossils they imprison. Once they were continuous over the mountain area, but with the upward thrust of the granite the sedimentaries became domed. (We call an upfold an *anticline*, and a downfold a *syncline*.) As the granite mass was thrust higher, the sedimentary blanket of rocks was eroded away. The story is told in the rocks. It is a simple story, and for one who cares to read it, it is lucidly told.

Nowhere is the evidence more dramatically or more obviously presented than at the Garden of the Gods at Manitou, Colorado. Some of the rocks in this foothill have been so bent that they are ninety degrees from the original horizontal. Erosion has worn away the softer rocks, leaving certain resistant layers stabbing at the sky in fantastic shapes. Sharp pinnacles, spires, natural bridges, narrow gateways, balanced rocks, and distorted, goblinlike forms—so grotesque in shape that they are spoken of as "hoodoos" in our Southwest—have resulted from erosion's chiseling. Deep-red sandstones, beds of cemented gravels, which we call conglomerate, hardened layers of clay or shale, and a conspicuous layer of whitish gypsum are so combined as to add variety and a certain weirdness to the landscape. The rock formations differ so much in their resistance to the agents of weathering and erosion that vertical walls of red sandstone forty to fifty feet high are left standing, while the neighboring beds of the softer shale are washed away. Mushroomlike forms develop where a mass of firm, hard rock caps a less resistant layer. The famous "balanced rock," where thousands of people have had their portraits taken by a local photographer who appropriated this spot as a studio, is due to a soft layer underlying a resistant bed of heavy sandstone. Most of the soft material has been washed or blown away, and the hard capstone remains on a very small

76

pedestal. These ridges are then but the piers or bastions of arched rocks that once covered the mountains. The structural relations of the Rocky Mountains are graphically presented at the end of the book. There the reader can discover for himself the wonders of geologic action.

East of the belt of almost vertical rock layers near Manitou, in the region of the Sky-Line Drive, and at many other places in the foothills of the front ranges of Colorado, Wyoming, and Montana, a series of inclined beds of sandstone stand out as hogbacks or pigbacks. Looking down from the air these barn-yard names seem quite appropriate. The great out-of-door theater, or auditorium, built by the people of Denver is in the foothill belt of the Rockies, where the layers of red sandstone and shale are inclined at an angle of about fifteen degrees.

This uplift of beds and subsequent erosion is better shown in the San Juan Range in southwestern Colorado. It is clear that here there was a huge dome, for the layers of sediments found around the margins slope in all directions away from the central portion of the range. There must have been an uplift in which 20,000 to 30,000 feet in layers of rock were involved in the doming. The summit of this tremendous dome has been entirely removed by erosion.

When approaching the San Juan Range from the north and traveling from Montrose to Ouray, we see inclined layers of rock on either side of the Uncompahgre Valley. As we proceed southward, these layers rise higher and higher until, at Ouray, they form rock walls 3,000 to 4,000 feet high. If we cross to the south side of the range, we find near Durango that the rock layers of the same age as those near Ouray decline

away from the mountain area. Here their slope, or dip, is sufficient to cause the development of hogback ridges. These layers
of rock were formerly continuous over the entire area of this
structural dome. We know that rocks are of the same age
when we find similar fossils or evidences of once living plants
or animals embedded in the rock layers.

This structural form of uplift and then erosion, exposing a
granite mountain core, flanked or surrounded with the remnants of the layers of stratified rock, gives a clue to the geologic
story of other sections of the Rockies. Again and again we discover the granite mountains surrounded by parallel ranges of
foothills.

In the case of the Uinta Range, in the northeastern part
of Utah, the layers of sediments, on the north and south
sides, slope away from the axis of a great fold. This is the
longest and most nearly symmetrical upfold having an east-
west axis in the entire Rocky Mountain province. Here the
pressure that caused the upfolding of the rock layers must
have come from the north and south. At the south margin of
the Uinta Range, the layers of rock slope gently southward
into the plateau region of the Green River. At the north, the
same layers, which formerly continued over the crest of the
great fold, slope northward. Here the mountain-making pressure was intense. The rocks are on edge at places, and there
is some evidence of breaking and slipping.

The central part of the Uinta fold is very broad, and there
the rock layers of varying hardness are nearly horizontal. This
condition has resulted, through long-continued erosion, in
the carving of many pyramidlike peaks out of the great rock

78

mass. The mountain forms resemble in outline the temples carved in the Grand Canyon of the Colorado, where the rock layers also are horizontal, and where they alternate in resistance to the agents of erosion. The harder, firmer layers form cliffs, while the less resistant beds furnish slopes of broken, angular rocks, which we know as talus.

In the Big Horn Basin in Wyoming there is a small but remarkably symmetrical, cigar-shaped mountain range which is so dissected that its structure is now very clearly defined. Here we have an anticlinal, or upfold, with an axis which plunges downward to the north and to the south. Each of the more resistant layers is a ridge maker, and where streams have crossed the upturned layers, they have cut water gaps or narrow gateways. The small streams flowing from the core outward to the margin of the range follow zigzag courses, avoiding the harder rocks as much as possible.

The route followed by thousands of tourists during normal times on their way to the east entrance of Yellowstone National Park passes directly through the Owl Creek Mountains at the spectacular pass of Thermopolis. This range, situated at the south margin of the Big Horn Basin, is another good example of an upfold that has undergone dissection. The layers of rock sediments slope away from the axis on either side, and in the center there are very ancient core rocks.

In the huge folds in the rocks of the crustal portion of the earth, we have discovered the commonest, or most widespread, of the Rocky Mountain structures. Some kind of folding has entered into the history of nearly all the mountains of the world, and it is exciting to our travel if we can recognize the

79

signs of such folding. Almost everywhere we go on our expeditions through the ranges of the Rocky Mountains we shall
see evidences of the upturning and bending of layers of rock
that were originally put down as fine sediments on the bottom
of some shallow inland sea that lay over a great portion of our
continent.

The uplift of great land masses is infinitely slow, often so
slow that weathering and erosion wore away surfaces almost as
rapidly as the uplift took place. Certainly, where rocks are
uplifted as a dome, the upper surface is ordinarily soon eroded
and destroyed, and mountain peaks and valleys come into
being. The whole earth movement is on so huge a scale, and
the time involved is so much longer than human history, that
the concept is a difficult one to grasp. But a great test of one's
credulity is found in the uplifted block, the broken fragment
of the earth's crust that fractured and was thrust upward. The
blocks are colossal, whole mountain ranges in themselves. Such
are the Tetons, in the northwestern corner of Wyoming. The
magnificent eastern mountain scarp is the break, the fault line,
of the uplifted block. Upward the rock was thrust into some
ancient geologic climate for seven thousand feet. As it rose, the
hungry forces of erosion attacked the block, cutting ravines and
canyons in the scarp. Later, glaciers gouged the valleys and
gave character to the peaks. The troughs through which some
of these glaciers moved are clearly defined on the east face
of the range. At their lower ends are charming lakes, which
reflect the rugged peaks and make this region one of the love-
liest of our national parks and a paradise for artists and photographers. Erosion by streams and ice has now continued for

more than a million years, and today in the Grand Tetons we have one of the most picturesque small mountain areas on the continent.

In northern Montana, near the International Boundary Line another great geological process occurred. Rock slipping took place on a remarkable scale, and a huge mountain mass moved eastward very slowly for a distance of about twenty-two miles. This is in the region set aside as Glacier National Park. The rock movement here is called thrust faulting, and the great mass, which includes all the mountains of the Park, and contains billions of tons of rock, traveled eastward over a gently inclined plane as pressure from the west continued. The mountain mass actually moved over the western margin of the Great Plains far beyond the present east base of the mountains. Chief Mountain is a remnant of that shifting mass. It is composed of the same rock formations as those in the Lewis and Clark Ranges of Glacier National Park, and therefore serves as testimony of the former eastward extent of the mountain mass, which was once unbroken. The rocks in Chief Mountain are very old, and they rest upon the comparatively young formations of the Great Plains.

Those who live in the man-made oasis surrounding Salt Lake City and Provo look up each day at the bold west face of the Wasatch Mountains of Utah. This range is carved out of another huge block that was lifted high above the floor of the Great Basin to the west. The bold mountain front is the face, or end, of that block. As the mountain mass rose, streams, winds, rains, and all agents of rock weathering helped to dissect the uplifted rock. Canyons were excavated and mountain peaks defined. Alpine glaciers formed in this range at least three times and moved from the summit areas to the foothill belt, transforming V-shaped canyons cut by mountain torrents into U-shaped gorges, and depositing great heaps of debris as moraines at the west margin of the range. Had men lived on this continent during any one of these ice periods, they would have found in the Wasatch and Uinta Ranges a Switzerland on a grand scale. No glacier in the Alps today can compare in size with the huge tongues of ice that formed among these American mountains in the earlier glacial periods.

There are other ranges in the Rockies which are blocks that have been uplifted and tilted, among them the Jefferson, Madison, Bitterroot, Beaverhead, and several others in western Montana. In some localities there has been so much faulting, or slipping, that the structures of the mountain ranges are exceedingly complex. Incidentally, they include some of the richly mineralized areas that supply our country with raw materials that are essential in important industries.

Where can folding and faulting best be viewed by the tourist? Where can these dramatic, almost terrifying, processes be observed?

The gateway west of Calgary, leading into the Canadian Rockies near Banff, is a great gorge cut by the Bow River. In the walls of that canyon the layers of rock are folded and mangled, and at several places there is clear evidence of slipping on a great scale. Before we reach the village of Banff, the valley through which we are traveling becomes broad and open, and we encounter glacial moraines and great outwash deposits left by waters which issued from beneath an ancient alpine river of ice.

To the north and south, bold mountain forms tower thousands of feet above the valley floor, and nowhere in these huge rock masses are the rock layers horizontal. They have all been disturbed during the making of the mountains, and now they stand at various angles. Here, again, we see many examples of folding and faulting in the growth of mountains.

A few miles upstream from Banff, we turn sharply to the south, climb about 500 feet, and, after traveling two or three miles over a great frontal moraine with a hilly, hummocky topography, suddenly come to one of the most beautifully situated lakes in the world. We are at the north margin of Lake Louise and are standing on the frontal moraine, made of boulders, sand, and clay brought by the ice, which holds the lake in place. The distant walls on either side are dark and somber, towering almost vertically for thousands of feet above the dark-blue waters of the lake. Almost exactly in the middle of the south shore of the lake there is a gap, or opening, through which we see Victoria Glacier, with Mt. Victoria on the distant sky line. Each year, during normal peacetime, thousands of visitors linger along the walks, or rest in the comfortable chairs of the Lake Château and enjoy this scene. Great white clouds float by above the mountain crest through the rich blue sky and, as the sun slowly changes in position with the earth's rotation, the high lights and deep shadows shift from place to place. The picture is perfect.

The rock layers in Mt. Victoria were formed in the sea.

83

They were then but sands, silts, and limy muds. They have been hardened and uplifted to elevations of 11,365 feet above tidal waters. Winds, rains, and streams helped to dissect the mountain mass. Snows came, and in time formed glaciers that descended far down the canyons excavated by the streams. Then a profound change in climate occurred; the snowfall decreased in amount, and the ice on the lower lands melted away. Victoria Glacier today is but a shrunken remnant of the glacier that formed the basin in which Lake Louise is situated. There is much of meaning and inspiration in this magnificent vista.

The modern highway from Banff northward to Jasper passes through some of the most interesting mountain country in the world. To the right, to the left, and directly ahead, stretch magnificent panoramas, mile after mile of thrilling grandeur. For the structural geologist, there are great rock folds and fault blocks of various kinds to view. For the glacialist, there are the heavy deposits left by the ice, sand and gravel outwash, hundreds of alpine glaciers, and an icecap thousands of square miles in extent. The forester or botanist is in a region of beautiful stands of spruce and pine, and, during the summer, in a land of flowering plants. A zoologist also finds this a rich region for a field season, for deer, bear, and mountain sheep run wild, birds are abundant, and the streams and lakes teem with fish.

From the veranda or lounge of the château near Mt. Athabaska, about midway between Lake Louise and Jasper, our outlook is equal once again to many of the famed scenic views of Switzerland. Ten miles of the Athabaska Glacier are directly before us. In the far distance we see a portion of the Columbia Icefield. Mt. Athabaska is a little to the left, its slopes mantled with small alpine glaciers. In the foreground icy waters find their way among heaps of morainic debris, so recently left by the retreating glaciers that they are barren masses of mud, gravel, boulders, and sand. The long, even-crusted ridge of debris at the left of the ice, bare of vegetation, is a lateral moraine. It resembles a great railroad embankment.

A few miles north of the Mt. Athabaska stop lie Mt. Kitchener and Dome Mountain, both rising precipitously from the valley floor and both capped by ice advancing from the Columbia Icefield to the rim of the great canyon through which our route of travel lies. As the ice moves slowly to the brink of the canyon and there breaks off, it maintains a 500-foot crystal-white cliff resembling the generous frosting of a wedding cake.

Near Jasper the highway valley is broad, with extensive meadowlands which provide sites for ranches, tourist camps, and the city of Jasper. For the first time in several days we hear the puff of locomotives, pulling passengers and freight into the mountains from Edmonton. The automobile highway now follows the same valley used by the railway between the mountains and the farmlands of the Great Plains of mid-western Canada. At the gateway on this route the mountains show signs of intense folding and bending, even more remarkable than those at the gateway west of Calgary. Throughout the Canadian Rockies we are in the midst of geologic structures involving both folding and faulting. Most of the great mountain ranges of the world are due to tremendous forces in

85

the crustal portion of the earth that have lifted, folded, mangled, crushed, and broken the rock formations. The uplifting movements and the carving of the great rock masses went on slowly, but at places on the earth's surface, such as we are now visiting, magnificent scenic features resulted, vast wealth became concentrated deep in the earth in certain of the cracks and crevices in the rocks, the uplifted masses modified the climate, presenting to man varied possibilities for making a living from the resources which appeared before him, or which he discovered still buried in the rock.

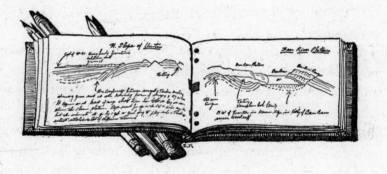

CHAPTER FOUR

FROM THE AIR
AND FROM THE SADDLE

While our assignment for field study calls for particular attention to the rock structures and the working out of the physical history of the several ranges in the Rocky Mountain region, we are not unmindful of a world of scenic beauty, various zones of plant and animal life at different altitudes, the climatic changes, and the ways in which mountainmen make a living. Remember that our mountain area extends from the semiarid portion of central New Mexico northward for at least 1,000 miles, reaching into the well-watered and heavily forested lands of the Dominion of Canada. Already we have visited the ranges as far north as Jasper, in Alberta, but the Rockies continue about 1,500 miles farther northward, even into Alaska. In width, our region of study varies up to about 300 miles. We are dealing with about 300,000 square miles of country, all interesting for one reason or another, and containing many superb natural wonderlands.

FROM THE AIR

If on a clear day we were flying westward over the Great Plains, before reaching Denver or Colorado Springs, we should see a line of snow-covered peaks a few hundred miles away on the western horizon. They rise in the midst of a sea of dark, forest-clad mountains. Huge billows of white cumulus clouds hover over the mountain crest almost every day during the summer season. About the summits there may be cloud banners streaming to the leeward of the peaks.

When the pioneers came westward on the surface of the land above which we may now fly at ease, the great mountain front was a real barrier to travel. Those early adventurers were forced to pause, abandon wagons and oxcarts, pack their outfits on the backs of animals, and plod over the mountain trails. Camps and trading stations were established where men, tired from the monotony of the plains, started eagerly on the mountain trail. Considerable trading must have gone on among the hardy pioneers, and the men who kept trading posts in those early days did a thriving business. The stopping places became villages, and some of them grew into large and important cities, such as Cheyenne, Greeley, Denver, Colorado Springs, and Pueblo. They are the gateway cities of today.

At few places in the world can we find such a striking change in the physical features of the earth's surface as at the west margin of the Great Plains in the United States and Canada. There a nearly level surface ends and a great rocky mass rises abruptly 2,000 to 8,000 feet. At its western margin the plain is

90

about a mile above sea level, but the summits of the higher mountains in the front ranges are 14,000 feet above tidal waters. From western Texas northward for at least 2,500 miles through the United States and far into the northern wilderness of Canada, beyond the crossing of the new Alaskan Highway, the east face of the Rocky Mountains is a nearly continuous bold and rocky escarpment.

When viewed from the air directly above the highland area, the mountain wall is one margin of a series of ranges, most of which have nearly north-south axes. The most notable exceptions are the Uinta and Owl Creek Ranges, which have east-west axes, and the Wind River Range, with a backbone that extends from the northwest to the southeast. In Canada the individual ranges are nearly parallel, and they are separated by deep troughs or trenches that extend northwestward from the International Boundary Line.

The highest crest-line peaks of the Rockies, snow-clad most of the year, are some distance back from the eastern margin of the mountain area, and roughly at an equal distance from the western edge of the great highland region.

New Mexico, Colorado, Utah, Wyoming, Montana, and the Canadian provinces of Alberta, British Columbia, and Yukon, all boast of lofty mountain summits which rise majestically into or above the clouds. Pikes Peak, Mt. Evans, Longs Peak, the Mountain of the Holy Cross, and Uncompahgre are the pride of Colorado. In Utah, Hayden, Gilbert, and Agassiz are among the highest peaks. In Wyoming, Fremont and Gannett in the Wind River Range, the Grand Teton in the range of the same name, and Cloud Peak in the Big Horns challenge the ambitious mountain climber and pose repeatedly for amateur photographers.

In Montana there are a dozen spectacular summits in the Lewis and Clark Ranges of Glacier National Park. In Canada, Mt. Robson is among the best known, but Athabaska, Mt. Victoria, Kitchener, and a score of others carry perennial snow fields and long alpine glaciers on their upper slopes. They are so high and so far north that they have, today, a charm that must have been present in hundreds of places in the mountain areas farther south during the last Great Ice Age. The Canadian Rockies are superb repositories of bold, rugged mountain scenery, valley glaciers, large icecaps, and, in the Columbia Icefield, a miniature continental ice sheet still exists.

When in the air, we realize that this vast mountain area contains many semienclosed lowlands. These, sometimes called basins and sometimes parks, are meadowlands with a fringe of forest trees about their margins, and their attractive ranch homes, rural villages, and irrigated farms give a human touch to the wilder mountain scene.

A trained observer can pick out, from a plane, the major features in the drainage patterns in the different sections of the Rocky Mountain system. These present many difficult problems. Why should each of the larger rivers in the Rocky Mountains, in the United States, cross through a giant mountain range instead of choosing an easier route? The Royal Gorge was excavated by the Arkansas River in crossing a mighty mountain range. The Black Canyon of the Gunnison is in some of the hardest and most resistant of rock formations. The Colorado River has cut several such gorges in getting from Middle Park to the plateau country west of the mountains. The Green River is responsible for Flaming Gorge in the Uintas, and the Wind River has cut the famous notch through the Owl Creek Range at Thermopolis. The Laramie, Shoshone, Big Horn, Missouri, Snake, and a dozen more streams have chosen, or have been forced, to excavate magnificent canyons through mountain ranges. These things did not happen by chance or accident. There is a fascinating story tied up in the history of drainage from this high mountain area, which will come out in a later chapter.

Why should the Columbia and the Kootenay Rivers part company on a meadowland when but a few rods apart, in the Rocky Mountain trench of Canada, to meet again after a series of interesting experiences? The Kootenay turns southward and, by a very circuitous route, makes a long detour into the United States, returns to Canada, and then joins the Columbia as a tributary. The Columbia, rising in a marshy land within a few feet of the Kootenay, flows northward, after a long journey turns southward, passes through several long lakes, receives the Kootenay, enters the United States, cuts a deep canyon in a great lava plateau, and then, by plunging into a gorge which it has made in the Cascade Range, finds its way to the sea. This peculiar stream pattern has been caused by the great ice sheet for, during the Glacial period, the ice forced the streams from their normal courses.

If we were in a helicopter high above the ranges of the Rocky Mountain area, perhaps the most striking feature we should see would be the thousand lakes of a blue deeper than the sky. They are like azurite beads of a rosary, strung as they are along cords of streams. Geologists call them "paternoster lakes." On their shores are many camps, tent sites and cabins. There, in the clear mountain air on the shores of the crystal waters, vacationists fish, bathe courageously in the cold waters, or lie on the warm rocks, taking comfort and health from the sun. The beauty of the mountain lake calls for the pen of a Ruskin: "In the mountains lakes are myriad, often unnamed and so hidden away that to the discoverer they seem a personal and original find."

There are also the larger lakes, most of them now famous resorts. In the United States, Jackson and Yellowstone Lakes, Coeur d'Alene, Pond Oreille, Flathead, Lake McDonald, and St. Mary's Lakes are best known. In Canada, small lakes high in the mountain area are numerous, and in the lowland troughs there are several remarkably long and beautifully situated lakes on which there is steamboat service. Waterton, Kootenay, and the Arrow Lakes are among the larger ones.

Mining towns and lonely mining camps are sprinkled through the mountain country. Some of these are busy places, noisy with the crash of the rock crushers or the rattle of the vibrating jig tables, called concentrating tables, on which the fragments of ore are separated from the pieces of rock. Others have little life today or are completely abandoned. They represent the high hopes of gold seekers, hopes that in some instances were fulfilled beyond all dreams, but in others were desperate and devastating failures. Though it was gold that lured the first prospectors, the mountains contain many other minerals. At times gold, copper, silver, lead, and zinc will be recovered from a single vein, and of these gold may be the

94

least in value. Some of the exploration was highly scientific and carried on by competent mineralogists, but much of it was haphazard searching by deluded gamblers, reckless men who counted on the wheel of chance more than on science. Other patient prospectors worked by rule of thumb. This latter class is the proverbial type, the lonely, bearded miner who, with no financial backers, few instruments, and no company but a donkey, searches out the remote gullies. Some of these men have found wealth. But thousands of prospect holes on the mountainsides record the forlorn hopes of pioneer mining men who failed. Stories of the discovery and development of mineral resources are legion, since hundreds of millions of dollars' worth of metallic ores have been taken from this territory; and all the fabulous wealth derived from the rocky expanse was created during the mountain history we are tracing.

The forests in the mountainous regions are on the middle slopes of the ranges. The valley lowlands are grasslands or, in the drier parts, overgrown with sagebrush. From the foothills upward, for three to five thousand feet, there is usually a zone of trees. The higher, or summit areas among the mountains are above the tree line. There we find the alpine grasses, flowering plants, and the pasturelands for hundreds of thousands of sheep.

FROM THE SADDLE

Mountains are exciting. Our airplane trip over the peaks is not satisfying, for we must explore the mountain face ourselves. We must be intimate with details hidden from us by the over-all view. One of the splendid experiences of the Rockies is horse travel, and everywhere we go horses are ready for us. It takes a lifetime to know a single mountain, yet certain facts stand out and are learned in a single trip from valley station to peak. Every observer is struck by the zones of forest and bush and animal life that are passed through as the trail mounts. We marvel at the rapidity with which life on mountain slopes changes with altitude. These zonings are represented not only by tree and flower, but by mammal and bird. Yet it is not only altitude that effects the change, but exposure to wind and sun, rock formations, and soil, as well.

In the lowlands bordering the range, we may be in the midst of greasewood and sagebrush, and the wild life, if any, will consist chiefly of coyotes, jack rabbits, sage hens, and prairie dogs. As we approach the foothills, we see dwarfed cedars and piñons, not as dense forest growth, but as scattered clumps, or groves, of trees. This lowest habitat has a semiarid climate. It is a seared, brown, dry, and dusty area, with few permanent homes for settlers.

Near the base of the range, where mountain streams flow through the canyons, ranches stocked with cattle, horses, and sheep are surrounded by fields of alfalfa, timothy, or peas, which provide fodder for the livestock during the winter season. Birds are abundant in this zone, and wild canaries, jays, bluebirds, Louisiana orioles, and song sparrows are all about us. We stop for lunch, and the camp robins appear. One can hardly lay down part of his biscuit before a knowing camp robin, or "robber," who has had his eye on it all the time, sidles up to take it off in his bill. One late afternoon, choosing a woodsy

96

spot, we pitched camp and nailed a temporary table between two small pines. At breakfast time, when we placed the first dish on the table, a beautiful hummingbird darted up from her tiny nest in a branch less than two feet from our faces. She repeated this when we came in for supper, but soon learned that we meant no harm and remained on her eggs, keeping her bright eye upon us as we ate.

Above the zone of ranch homes we enter the more densely forested belts on the mountain slopes. Pines and quaking aspens and, a little higher, fragrant spruces and firs predominate. Among these forest trees many of the ranchmen's cattle and horses graze. If our eyes are alert, we may see deer, antelope, bears, foxes, wildcats, elk, moose, beavers, and many of the more timid forest birds.

Climbing still higher on the mountain slope, we run into a belt of dwarfed trees that include junipers and cedars. Here are excellent examples of trees and shrubs that have been bent low by the winds, some of them growing more horizontally than vertically, resembling green mattresses spread over the ground. In time we pass above the tree line into the zone of grasses, mosses, low-flowering plants, and large areas of bare rock.

Among these high-altitude plants the ptarmigan, the snow bunting, and the marmot are at home. The whistling marmots in the high mountain regions announce their presence boldly, but, to avoid discovery, they remain motionless. Grasses occupy all the high alpine benchlands and basins wherever there is sufficient soil. They are exceedingly luxuriant and provide excellent summer pastures. The alpine flora include an abun-

97

dance of blooming plants, and during the summer large areas of the mountainsides are veritable flower gardens. All plant forms are stunted, for the growing season is so short that there is little time for producing long stems. But blossoms are exceptionally large. Here we find the brilliant red and yellow Indian paintbrush, the larkspur, lupine, monk's cap, daisy, saxifrage, gentian, and a hundred more, growing in profusion at varying altitudes in the mountain area. Beside the stream near the bottom of the trail, the lupine may be three or four feet tall. Near the peaks it fairly hugs the rock, but sends up a brave banner of flowers. In some of the crannies among the rocks in high places we find the Rocky Mountain columbine, Colorado's state flower. Its rich purple or blue, combined with creamy white or faint lavender, adds a bit of delicate and rare beauty to the mountain landscape.

Still higher, above the grassy fields, a great variety of lichens of different colors and textures cling to the bare rock surfaces and those who look closely may find tiny red algae living on the snow near the mountain summits. We do not get above all plant or animal life. The snow bunting and ptarmigan are with us, and, high overhead, eagles float back and forth, searching for game to take to their little ones in a nest on the top of some rocky pinnacle.

FROM AN OUTLOOK STATION

When we have passed the tree line and climbed above the flower-blanketed alpine fields, we come to the region of rocky crags and the land of perennial snows. Here is our vantage point, our ultimate goal, our personal conquest of the peak. And, as a seasoned mountain climber, let me warn you again, now is the time to don that sweater or windbreaker. The exertion of the climb has opened the pores of the body and though the sunshine is warm, the chilling wind is penetrating and dangerous. But no one can prepare you for the sense of beauty and serenity that comes as you gaze out over an almost limitless horizon. The scene gives you a feeling of detachment from earth itself. We may be at the crest of the wall of a gigantic canyon, three, four, or five thousand feet deep. The slope is precipitous, and if we happen to loosen one of the huge, angular blocks of rock all about us, it will tumble over and over again in its descent, bounding far into the air as it passes over one cliff after another. The chances are that it will be broken into a thousand parts, and the last sign we see of the aid we have given to the force of gravity is a cloud of dust swirling thousands of feet below, where fragments of the huge block have come to rest.

We may be on the rim of a large amphitheatral basin at the head of one of the mountain canyons. The walls are nearly vertical, and, as weathering proceeds, rock fragments of all sizes, grading up to five feet or more in length, fall and form conelike accumulations of talus, or great aprons of angular fragments, which mantle the margin of the basin. Where talus accumulations are very heavy in the high alpine basins, they have taken on the characteristics of coarse-grained mudflows. Ice forms in the open spaces in these heaps of mountain debris,

99

huge quantities of water from melting snow are added to the mass, and movement begins. Thus we see with our own eyes how rock streams or rock glaciers are formed.

In the great circuslike basin before us the bare rock surfaces carry scratches cut by rock fragments frozen into the ice that moved over the basin floor. These scratches illustrate how the basin was formed. Snows accumulated and in time formed a glacier. The ice froze around the loose material on the basin floor, and thus the ice became shod with rock. It moved into the valley or canyon below, and as it advanced, it scratched, grooved, and polished the rock surfaces over which it moved. Here and there the ice gouged out minor basins in the solid rock, and those are now occupied by the deep-blue or green lakes we see below our outlook station. The walls of the basin became steepened, as materials were carried away at the base, retreating as the process continued; and in time a large amphitheatral space, or cirque, was carved out in the summit area of the range.

We are sitting on the rim of just such a cirque, where a glacier formed, and from which ice descended for miles and miles through the great canyon beyond, giving the gorge a U-shaped form. Later the ice melted away, leaving heaps of debris, which explain the ponds of the stream and the formation of the chain of beautiful lakes glimpsed far down the valley. In the immediate foreground the glacial cirque and the cirque lakes record a gigantic amount of work accomplished, climatic changes of a major kind, and more than a million years of earth history.

In the distance, beyond the range on which we are located,

Devils Tower. An ancient laccolith in eastern Wyoming. This rises four hundred feet above the surrounding lands.

Ship Rock, Arizona, and the Great Dyke.

The Spanish Peaks in the Colorado Rockies. In the foreground, the bold rock wall is due to a nearly vertical sheet of lava, a dyke, which is resisting erosion more effectively than the surrounding materials. Other lesser dykes appear at the left.

Folded strata. One place in Glacier National Park where the strata are distinctly folded.

is the crest line of another of the ranges in the Rocky Mountain system. Lofty, snow-capped peaks, huge arenalike basins, steep canyon walls with waterfalls, the forest-covered zone, and, in the lowlands between the ranges, a grassy meadowland, are all within our view.

A great cumulo-nimbus cloud is forming over the distant range, but we are far enough away to be perfectly safe. The summit of a range is not a good place to be when a thunderhead is hovering about. For one thing, discharges of electricity between the clouds and the mountaintops are exceedingly dangerous. Since the warm air near a human body is a good conductor, a flash of electricity headed for the mountain may choose to make its actual contact through your body. I have known men to be killed by such flashes of lightning on mountaintops, and I have felt my own hair stand erect, and tingling sensations pass through my body at their coming.

When viewed from a safe distance, a thunderstorm in the mountains is a magnificent spectacle. The large, dark, billowy masses of cloud roll over and over, each mass apparently trying to be on top. About its margin the cloud is thin and grayish or white, and surrounding the whole gigantic form, two or three miles in diameter, is the clear, blue, luminous sky. Sometimes streaks of sunlight break through openings in the clouds, illuminating the great storm, and with long golden streamers they pick out small patches of landscape below, which seem like exquisite miniature paintings.

The storm cloud throws a deep, foreboding shadow on the mountain below. That shadow moves forward as the cloud travels on its way about the margin of some great cyclonic

101

center of which it is a part. Winds become violent, for the storm center is evidence of great changes in air pressure within short distances. Trees are blown down; loose materials are taken high into the air; lightning flashes in long zigzags from cloud to mountaintop. The flash is seen instantaneously, and some moments later the sound of thunder reaches us. Now the show is on. Jagged streaks scar the sky at short intervals, and the roll of thunder hammers out a roaring cannonade that threatens to go on forever, as its echoes rebound from wall to wall within the mountain fastness.

Mountain storms are wild and fearsome. They bring to mind Shelley's inspiring lines from "The Revolt of Islam":

> So as I stood, one blast of muttering thunder
>> Burst in far peals along the waveless deep,
> When, gathering fast, around, above, and under,
>> Long trains of tremulous mist began to creep,
>> Until their complicating lines did steep
> The orient sun in shadow:—not a sound
>> Was heard; one horrible repose did keep
> The forests and the floods, and all around
> Darkness more dread than night was poured upon the ground.

Sir Martin Conway was one of the great alpinists. More than that, he was a close observer of nature, writing of the massing clouds in "The Alps": "Generally, after some preliminary skirmishing, the moment comes when they gather themselves together, as by word of command, and, coming on in united force, swallow up the mountain world. This final onrush is often a most magnificent and solemn sight. The gathering squadrons of the sky grow dark. . . . Their crests impend. They assume terrific shapes. . . . They do not so much seem to blot out as to destroy the mountains."

But mountain storms, fierce and awe-inspiring as they are, last but a few minutes. The wind beats at the aspen grove, the lightning crackles, and, as always in mountain valleys, there is the roar of the stream. Then rain begins to fall. A gray haze, or gauze, appears to hang from the cloud, like a veil with a frayed edge. For some time the rain does not reach the land surface. The tiny globules of water that comprise the cloud are absorbed by the thirsty air. Then contact is made between cloud and land, the gray haze reaches the ground, and the downpour from the cloud begins to wet the earth. Within a few minutes the soils are soaked, the streams are quickened, new rivulets form and tumble over precipices. The rivers from that section become torrents, for we are witnessing a real cloudburst. The running waters tear down through their all-too-narrow channels, dragging huge trees and rolling immense boulders to lower and lower levels. Many of the streams overflow their banks and spread sand, gravel, boulders, and all kinds of vegetable life, torn from the mountain-side, over the bottom lands of their valleys. The waters are yellow, for they are loaded with soils and fine rock materials. If settlements stand too near the seething current, houses, sheds, wagons, and livestock may be carried away. A cloudburst in the mountains is both magnificent and terrible. Like all tragic scenes, it has its thrill and its pathos. However, in most cases, the cloudbursts on the mountains strike in wilderness areas and do little or no damage to man or beast.

At last the great storm cloud spends its energy and fades

away, or moves on to some more distant range. The sky clears, and the warm rays of the sun pour down on the drenched landscape. . . . We have spent a very profitable hour or two on a mountaintop. The panorama before us is now full of meaning. It displays evidence of some of the gigantic forces of nature, revealing their agency in mountain making. Profound changes in climate, which took millions of years, are indicated in the records of glaciation. The carving of the mountain mass has involved the removal of millions of tons of earth material. This also has taken a long time. We have witnessed a spectacular demonstration of electric power in the atmosphere and waters pouring from the sky upon the rock. In addition to all the phenomena of earth building and earth disintegration and change, we have looked upon a scene of breath-taking beauty in form and coloring—forms no mortal sculptor can carve, colors no mortal artist can paint.

CHAPTER FIVE

UNDERSTANDING
MOUNTAIN SCENERY

THE NATURE AND MEANING OF CORE-ROCKS

So far we have read the history of our mountains merely from the upturning of the beds, or layers of rock, which form the foothills. But what is the story of the core rock, the granite blocks that compose the great mountain mass? Advancing from the margin of a folded mountain range toward the core, we usually pass from the youngest layers involved in the folding to the oldest of all the rock formations in that range. This is dramatically illustrated at many places, but nowhere better than in the Black Hills of South Dakota, which are an outlying range of the Rocky Mountains. In this range we are dealing with an elongated dome. It is one of the most symmetrical and simple mountain structures in the world. It is the Rocky Mountain range in miniature.

From north to south, the uplifted Black Hills area extends about eighty miles; in width, about thirty-five miles. Everywhere about the base of the range the rock layers are upturned. On the east, north, and south they stand at rather high angles, but on the west they are gently inclined. Here they rise from the Great Plains of Wyoming and lap up over the western part of the mountain mass, forming a plateaulike area in that portion of the Black Hills.

One of the best ways to examine the sequence of rock formations in the range is to approach the Hills from the east, near Rapid City, continue westward through one of the canyons into the heart of the mountain area, and then turn to Harney Peak.

East of the range you are in a district of nearly horizontal beds. These are wonderfully exposed in some of the Bad Lands of southwestern South Dakota. Here mountain-making movement has not disturbed the rock layers. A layer of sod, bound together by the roots of grass, has served for centuries as a protecting cover, but wherever that sod has been removed by a sudden downpour of rain, or has been undercut by strong winds, the underlying soft clay has been fashioned into fantastic hoodoos. The lands are "bad," because they are without much vegetation, and so rough that they are useless, except for sight-seeing purposes. A large area has been set aside as a national monument. Excellent highways and overnight camps or lodges have been provided and travelers may journey deep into the heart of this weird landscape, and still find comfortable accommodation.

In the foothill belt of the Black Hills the youngest of the upturned layers which give us the date when the mountains were born are exposed in low ridges and valley walls. They are much older than the layers of clay and sand in the Bad Lands, but as the ages of rocks are figured, they are not very old. In comparison with the Friendly Mountains of New England

108

and the Great Smokies and the Blue Ridge of the Carolinas and Virginia, the Rockies are very young. The older mountains in the eastern part of North America had passed through millions of years of various kinds of adventures before the Rocky Mountains were born.

Below the outer foothill layers, and upturned a little nearer the center of the Black Hills, come several hundred feet of deep-red rocks which give a pronounced color character to a part of the foothill belt on the east side of the range. They are the same formations as those encountered in the Garden of the Gods and in the foothill belts of many of the ranges in the Rocky Mountain system. Next come the great layers of blue-gray limestone and shales, or clay rocks. They carry the fossils of animals that lived a few million years earlier than any of those represented in the rocks of the Bad Lands or in the foothill belts.

As we advance farther into the Hills, we find on our trail, and at either side in the rock walls, older and older formations, until, at last, in the core of the range, we see rocks as old as those known anywhere in the earth's crust. These oldest of all known things command interest and respect. They have passed through more vicissitudes, been crushed and mangled in more mountain-making movements, been affected by more volcanic disturbances of all kinds during the history of the earth, than any other rock formations. Since they are at the bottom, below all other known rocks, they must have been deformed over and over again, as mountains were made.

The forces that make mountains are deep seated. They come from far below the surface and affect everything above them. The molten rocks associated with volcanic action all come from deep below the surface of the earth. They must have started at depths of at least twenty miles. As they worked their way upward, they must, of necessity, have passed into or through these most ancient rock formations, which today we find exposed in the core of the Black Hills and in the cores of many mountain ranges.

This oldest of all rock systems is the pre-Paleozoic, the basement rocks of the earth. They are so old and have undergone so much stress and strain, so much contortion and change, that we cannot read from them their original condition. But imperfect fossils imbedded in them show that a low form of life did exist in the pre-Paleozoic times, and the Paleozoic era was one of abundant and advanced life. In the first Paleozoic period there were trilobites, crawfishlike animals, and various forms of shell life. The period is one primarily of marine animal life. Later in the Paleozoic time came the fish. But not until mid-Paleozoic eras did treelike plants appear.

Thus the pre-Paleozoic rock mixture contains the altered rocks that have been tremendously mangled. Under pressures continuing through long periods of time and accompanied by great heat, the original rock materials have been profoundly altered. The changes presumably took place at depths of five to ten miles below the surface of the earth in the zone of rock flowage. Here, rock is molten, or so hot that it can flow, but because of the great pressure no cracks can exist, and the rock remains almost immovable. The heat associated with the deep-seated changes in the rocks may have been produced in part by pressure, in part by chemical changes, and in part may have come up from the depths in the earth, where great heat is always present.

New minerals, such as the micas and garnets, were formed as compression went on. Certain of the minerals were stretched out, giving a banded texture to rocks. Some students of metamorphism (rock change under great pressure) hold that, given time, pressure, and sufficient heat, there is nothing in nature that will change more profoundly than the minerals. Those that have been rearranged in bands have developed rocks that are called gneisses, or schists. These are the commonest of altered rocks, and they are found in the core of the Black Hills and in the cores of most of the ranges of the Rocky Mountains. We shall encounter these very ancient rocks also in the depths of many of the most picturesque gorges. Since they have been through several periods of change, have been crushed, broken, contorted, heated, and cooled, there is nothing monotonous about them. They differ greatly within short distances; and blazon forth in a great variety of colors and textures. At some places, these ancient rocks are so fine-grained that the unaided eye cannot detect the individual minerals; at other places, large crystal forms attract the collector, and gems and semiprecious stones, such as rubies, amethysts, tourmalines, and clear-quartz crystals, may be found.

At Harney Peak, the most picturesque area in the Black Hills, we are in the midst of an immense mass of pink granite, which was intruded, or thrust upward, from deep within the earth into the metamorphic rocks that constitute the core of the Black Hills. The Harney Peak granite is broken by several systems of joints or fractures, and, as weathering has taken place and great blocks of rock have fallen, sharp pinnacles and spires have been isolated. On one of the rounded surfaces of this great granite intrusion, Gutzon Borglum, the sculptor, worked for fourteen years, carving heroic bas-relief portraits of Washington, Jefferson, Lincoln, and Theodore Roosevelt. A large portion of the Harney Peak area has been set aside as a reservation.

In studying any mountain range, we anticipate that when we reach the central portion of the mountain mass or are in the depths of some great canyon where stream erosion has dissected far into the core of the mountains, we shall find some of the pre-Paleozoic or oldest of rock formations. These rocks appear in the heart of the San Juan Range of southwestern Colorado, and constitute the Needle Mountains of that range. They form the central and lofty portion of the front ranges of Colorado, and are exposed in the walls of the Royal Gorge of the Arkansas and the Black Canyon of the Gunnison. Pikes Peak, Longs Peak, Mt. Evans, Scraggly, and Little Scraggly, and the Mountain of the Holy Cross are composed of these most ancient rock formations.

Much of the Wind River (Wyoming) summit area, and Flattop, one of the interesting mountains of that range, are made up of this very ancient complex. Cloud Peak and other lofty summits in the Big Horn Range, the core of the Beartooth Range, the spectacular peaks of the Tetons, and the picturesque summits of the Purcell and Selkirk Ranges of Canada are composed of these oldest of rocks. The Tetons are really in the core of a mountain range, but the eastern half of that range has been dropped out of sight and buried. Elsewhere, as in the Uinta Mountains and in the Lewis and Clark Ranges of the Glacier National Park, the ancient pre-Paleozoic complex retains something of the original bedded structure. Farther north in the Canadian Rockies, the central mass of the mountains is formed of river-deposited sedimentary rock: limestones, shales (scaly rock), sandstones, and conglomerates, or rocks consisting of a mixture of rounded pebbles and hardened sediment. In Canada, then, the peaks may not be granite at all, but sedimentary rock formations.

The ancient and metamorphosed rocks assume a most fantastic mountain architecture, in the form of irregular pinnacles and an infinite variety of grotesque shapes. Many such are found in the Harney Peak region and the Tetons; whereas elsewhere the granite shows rounded summits, as in central Wyoming.

There is deep significance to the core rocks. Older than man's mind can encompass, they represent great age, titanic earth pressures, heat that changed the very character of the minerals, and volcanic action. By such huge and terrific forces were the mountains formed. Then came long periods of erosion, or wearing away, of the rock. Records show that at times the mountain areas were depressed until sea waters covered the area. We know this because of the sediments which were laid down in those seas, and then, in later mountain-making periods, were uplifted. The commonest evidence of marine origin, of course, is the fossils that are discovered in a given territory. This is a restless earth, and cycles of geologic time are measured by great uplifts, slow but inevitable erosion, and again uplift.

I suppose the built-up volcanic peak is the simplest of mountain concepts. But, though the shape is apt to be symmetrical, the structure of a volcanic mountain is not simple. It is marvelously interesting in its complexity. A volcano is not necessarily a mountain. Actually, it is a hole from which material is ejected, resulting in a volcanic cone, or in a lava plateau. The molten rock pouring from a volcano contains gases which are lost when the flowing mass hardens into lava.

THE STORY OF VOLCANIC PEAKS

The Rocky Mountains boast of no active volcanoes today, although within the mountain area and about its margins there are excellent examples of all kinds and varieties of volcanic activity.

Near the southern margin of Colorado rise the Spanish Peaks, huge monuments to volcanic eruption. West Spanish Peak has an elevation of 13,623 feet, and the summit of East Peak is but 915 feet lower. The most common preliminary announcements of the birth of a volcano are ominous rumblings, echoing deep-seated, subterranean explosions, earthquakes, indicative of slight movements in the crustal portion of the earth, and the emanation of gases. As molten rock approaches the surface it dissolves or amalgamates and absorbs the material into which it is moving. As the process continues, great heat is brought nearer and nearer to the surface, gases are released, water is vaporized, and any cracks or fissures that are present are filled with the fluid rock.

Molten rock has risen toward the surface of the earth at thousands of places without giving rise to true volcanoes. After cooling and solidifying, it remains as sheets or plugs of crystalline rock in the midst of other kinds of rock; or, occasionally, the molten material is forced in between other layers of rock. During the process of erosion that follows, the vertical masses of lava rock may be left standing, upright as monuments, or as ledges on the hillsides. Localities like the Spanish Peaks, in Colorado, where thousands of great eruptions occurred, are exceptions; there are far more places in the earth where the molten rock tried but failed to reach the surface than where true volcanoes came into existence.

In the building of the Spanish Peaks, the first eruption presumably threw into the air the overlying cover of sedimentary rocks. These sandstones, limestones, shales, and any other rocks directly above the rising mass of molten material were blown into fragments of various sizes. The ejected materials settled within and about a miniature crater, and are now at the base of these gigantic peaks. Molten rock may have surged and overflowed the rim of the crater many times, and added a few feet in thickness to the mass on one side or the other. Time after time, the fluid rock in the throat of the volcano may have cooled and frozen over. Again and again molten rock rose, to blow off the crest, heave vast quantities of fragmental materials into the air, and, by overflowing, add to the stature of the mountains. Thousands of such explosions and thousands of such outpourings occurred in the building of the Spanish Peaks. When the mass became very large, and consequently very heavy, outbreakings occurred on the sides. Lavas rose in great fissures about the craters and forced their way in between layers of rocks about the base of the mountains.

In the life history of a volcano there is a long period of growth. It may take decades or centuries to build a mass 6,000 to 10,000 feet high. A single layer of ash or dust may be, on the average, not more than an inch in thickness. That inch represents one explosion. A single lava flow may add anywhere from two or three feet up to fifty feet to the mountain mass. The flows are commonly not more than ten feet thick. All evidence found in the structure of volcanic mountains points to frequent eruptions and numerous outpourings of lavas in their upbuilding.

During the history of volcanic mountains, there may be long periods of inactivity, or dormancy. Rains fall on the mass of debris, valleys are cut, and when the next outpourings come, they follow the valley lines and do not add to the height of the mountain. At some places glaciers have formed during the period of mountain growth. The ice has descended to the base of the mountain, climatic changes have come, the glaciers have disappeared, and vulcanism has been renewed. We have proof that in the growth of some volcanoes there have been two, and even three, periods of glaciation. Since climatic changes, which cause the formation and disappearance of glaciers, take very long periods of time, even one glacial period during the growth of a mountain has great significance. It may represent several hundred thousand years.

None of the great volcanic peaks under discussion was constructed in a short period of time, and the process of wearing away or destruction, which we shall consider later, will prove equally long, or longer. As yet, not more than the first half of the life history of a volcano has been sketched.

The Spanish Peaks rise in the midst of huge quantities of lava material and, radiating from this center, there are scores of vertical, or nearly vertical, sheets of lava, or dikes. These stand out today, because of their superior resistance to erosion, as huge rock walls, extending for miles across the landscape, some of them as high as fifty feet above their surroundings. The dikes vary up to a hundred feet in thickness.

In the rock structure immediately surrounding these extinct or dormant volcanoes, there are sheets of lava between layers of other kinds of rock, called sills, since they outcrop and project about the margin of the plateau upon which the volcanoes are built.

A few miles southeast of the Spanish Peaks is Raton Mesa, seen by all who follow the highway from Trinidad, Colorado, to Raton, New Mexico. A great lava cap preserves that conspicuous tableland. Here the black lavas range from two hundred and fifty to five hundred feet in thickness. In one of the cliffs, eight distinct surface flows have been identified.

Immediately adjoining the Rocky Mountains in New Mexico, but a little to the west of the main ranges, is the Mt. Taylor theater of volcanic activity, with a central peak rising to 11,389 feet above the sea. Its growth must have been similar to that of the Spanish Peaks. Extensive lava flows spread in all directions from this focus, and about the base of the mountain there are a number of great pillars, or monuments, of black lava rock, varying from fifty to two hundred feet in height.

Nowhere on the continent is there a more spectacular volcanic mass than at Ship Rock, New Mexico, near the northwest corner of the state. That spire, pointing about eighteen hundred feet above its surroundings, is clearly visible from the summits of the San Juan Mountains of Colorado. Extending from the volcanic hulk is one of the most striking lava walls in all North America.

When the work of erosion or destruction exceeds growth, and a volcano begins to decrease in height and volume, we may think of the mountain as having passed its prime. As old age advances, the dissection of the cone continues, the valleys become deeper and wider, more tributary valleys are developed, and more and more of the mountain is carried away. The part to remain standing longest will be the hardest or most resistant. The last molten rock to rise in the throat of the volcano and cool there is certain to be very solid rock, much more resistant to erosion than the slopes of the mountain, which are made up of fragmental materials and lava flows. Since the throat filling is best protected, it is almost certain to remain longest, and to survive as the last conspicuous record of the location of an ancient volcano. These rocks that cooled in the throats of volcanoes and remained longest are called the volcanic plugs, or necks. Such forms appear in the vicinity of many of the great centers of volcanic action. They mark the location of volcanoes that have been destroyed by erosion.

In the evolution of the San Juan Mountains of southwestern Colorado, there came a time, late in geologic history, when volcanic activity broke forth with tremendous violence at many centers. Huge quantities of lava were poured out on

118

a great truncated dome, one hundred miles from west to east, and fifty miles from north to south. Upon these lavas millions of tons of ejected fragmental material accumulated. Every time a violent eruption occurred, vast quantities of dust, cinders, and angular bits of rock were thrown high above the volcanic vent. This material settled through the air and added another layer to the growing mass. When cemented into rock, such materials are breccias (angular conglomerates) or volcanic tuffs (rocks of cemented ash). At places in this range the products of one explosion are not, on the average, more than one inch thick. There must have been over 20,000 explosions, therefore, to make a mass of fragmental debris 2,000 feet in thickness. Since there are numerous layers of fragmental materials which have been cemented into rock, many of them more than 2,000 feet thick, there must have been a brilliant pyrotechnic display of over 100,000 eruptions from hundreds of vents in the building of the San Juan volcanic plateau. In addition to the fragmental materials, lava flows poured forth from time to time. The great mass of rock which came from deep within the earth was at places at least 10,000 feet thick. The lavas and breccias of the mountain region have been removed in part, and are everywhere deeply dissected.

Many of the picturesque peaks of the San Juans have been carved out of this volcanic plateau. You will recall our climb of Uncompahgre and a number of the peaks we saw from that elevated position. Mt. Sneffels, which we saw to the southwest, is a great volcanic plug, the last lava to cool in the throat of the volcano. Its summit, over 14,000 feet above the sea, is the center of an ancient volcano, which may have risen many thousands of feet above the present crest of the mountain. The throat rock in this great peak is coarsely crystalline, which means that it cooled slowly, and presumably under at least 4,000 or 5,000 feet of rock. An enormous amount of erosion has therefore taken place in these mountains since the volcanic plateau was built.

Before the Gunnison River could cut the magnificent gorge through which it courses, the river found it necessary to cut hundreds of feet through great lava flows blanketing the region between the San Juans on the south and the Elk Mountains to the north.

West of the San Juan Mountains, near the west margin of Colorado and in eastern Utah, there are several huge volcanic mountains. Ute Peak, Abajo Mountains, and the La Sal Mountains, are all due to large masses of molten material forced into the rocks near the surface of the earth. The molten rock caused the uplifting or doming of the overlying rocks, and erosion has since then uncovered the core. The most famous mountains of this type in North America, the Henry Mountains, are a little farther west on the plateau of Utah. Though they can hardly be considered within the compass of the Rocky Mountains, they are nonetheless a most fascinating region to visit.

Those who have crossed from Salida, Colorado westward to Gunnison on the narrow gauge of the Denver and Rio Grande Western Railroad will recall the long, slow climb and the chug-chug of the little engines shuttling back and forth on the sides of Ouray Peak. As the train approaches Marshall Pass, you may see from the observation platform something

120

of the old crater of that volcano, which has long been dormant. It is on the crest of the range, west of Salida.

In the west-central part of Colorado, north of the Gunnison River and east of Grand Junction, is Grand Mesa, a good example of a tableland capped with lava. Farther to the northeast, and west of the Park Range in Colorado, are the so-called Flattop Mountains. They are preserved by a cap of dark, fine-grained lava. In the Ten Mile District, a short distance north of Leadville and near the center of the state, there is a mining area, where sheets of lava have been thrust between great layers of limestones, sandstones, and shales.

In the northern portion of the Black Hills of South Dakota, and in the neighboring plains, there are indications of doming due to lavas. To the west of the Hills in Wyoming is the famous Devils Tower, which has been set aside as a national monument. This huge pillar of columnar lava was once in the throat of a volcanic mountain.

This columnar lava has six-sided columns, the symmetrical hexagonal cross-section resulting from certain strains set up within the rock as it cooled and shrank. The most familiar example is the Giant's Causeway on the north coast of Ireland. If we could get a good cross-section of this huge monument, the system of cracks that define the ends of the columns would remind us of mud cracks. When mud dries, it shrinks, and the cracks begin to open. When lava cools, it shrinks, the cracks form at the surface where the cooling takes place first, going deeper and deeper as the cooling continues. That is why we find lavas with columnar structures. The mass of material that formerly surrounded and covered Devils Tower has been removed by erosion. The last lava to rise through the vent was very resistant, and it is now left standing in impressive fashion about twelve hundred feet above its surroundings.

East of the main ranges of the Rocky Mountains in Montana are the Little Rockies, Bear Paw, Highwood, Little Belt, Big Snowy, and Crazy Mountains. These are outlying centers of mountain growth, where volcanic activity has been a dominant factor. West of the main ranges in Wyoming and south of the mountain areas of Idaho, are the extensive lava flows of the Snake River region, comprising one of the most famous lava plateaus in the world. At places the flows aggregate 5,000 feet in thickness. They have buried an ancient mountain topography, which is now exposed in profile on the walls of the Snake River Canyon.

A visit to the Craters of the Moon, on the surface of the Snake River lava flows, just south of the Rocky Mountains of Idaho, is an extraordinary adventure. The entire area has been set aside as a national monument. These craters exhibit remarkably well very recent volcanic activities, with lava flows that seem to have been poured out but a few days ago. They are as fresh in appearance as some of those in Hawaii and other centers where volcanic action has occurred in historic time. There are cones made of cinders thrown from volcanoes, with large craters in their summits; small cones, where eruptions took place from within lava flows; and long tunnels beneath the lava, where the surface hardened and the rest of the lava flowed on. Some of the cinder cones are as difficult to climb as a fresh sand dune, for the footing is uncertain, and with every step you slip back about as far as you advance.

Among the Craters of the Moon there are striking examples of some remarkable tree molds, which were formed where hot lavas accumulated around huge trees and then cooled. The trees burned completely, and today the lava molds of those trees are left standing. You can actually see the markings of the bark of those ancient trees on the inner walls of the molds.

The area of most unusual examples of volcanic activity in the Rocky Mountain region, the prize exhibit, is in the region of Yellowstone National Park and the Absaroka Range, east of the Park. In the Absarokas, the lava flows and the fragmental materials from the volcanoes constructed a great volcanic plateau, resembling the accumulations in the San Juan Range of southwestern Colorado. It, too, has been dissected into bold and rugged mountains.

In Yellowstone Park, the lavas are well exposed at many places. The obsidian cliffs on the main highway south from Mammoth Hot Springs are lavas that came to the surface and were chilled so suddenly that they changed into glass. The mass is brown or black, but, when examined with a microscope it is seen to be without a crystalline texture. There was not sufficient time for crystallization to take place. It is a true glass, naturally made.

In the northern part of the Park, near Tower Falls, lava flows with columnar structure are wonderfully well exposed on the walls of small canyons. Whole lava flows have been turned into hexagonal columns, which appear on the walls of a valley, like a row of stone posts. The brilliantly colored gorge of the Yellowstone is cut to a depth of 1,000 to 1,200 feet into lavas. Here the disintegration of the rocks has been accompanied by heat and vapors, with resulting shades of brown, red, and yellow that glorify them into a natural scenic marvel of astounding and incomparable beauty. In a climb to the summit of Mt. Washburn, many varieties of volcanic rock may be seen, and at Electric Peak, in the western part of the Park, another example of volcanic action is exhibited.

Those features, other than the canyon of the Yellowstone, which have made the park most famous and have attracted millions of visitors, are the hot springs, geysers, mud pots, and mud volcanoes. They are all secondary phenomena associated with the closing stages of volcanic action, and they will, in time, cease all activity. In many other portions of the continent there is evidence of similar activities that have died out completely. Those in Yellowstone Park are decreasing in violence. Even Old Faithful is waiting a little longer between eruptions than it did when discovered, in the seventies of the last century. Most of the geysers are irregular in their periods of eruption, and many of the hot springs have become inactive during the last two decades. Without the hot waters flowing over the limy terraces about the springs, the algae, which tinted the formations in beautiful colors, have died, leaving the terraces stony white. There are many places in the park where geysers or ordinary hot springs were formerly active.

THE GROWTH AND DECAY OF MOUNTAINS

The recent spectacular birth and growth of the Mexican volcano, Paracutin, rising in the midst of a cornfield, is exceptional. Most mountain-making movements take place with infinite slowness. Perhaps they have functioned as rapidly during the last hundred years as in any century in the history of the world. We are probably correct in thinking of their proceeding so slowly that, had people lived on the earth during the earlier periods of mountain growth, they might not have noticed changes in the mountains any more than we do today. Volcanoes are the only mountains that grow with dramatic display.

Earthquakes are signs of mountain growth. They are caused when large masses of the earth slip two or three inches or more along fissure planes. Today we have great landslides, which may be due to the result of sudden movements in a mountain mass undergoing uplift. Hot springs and geysers indicate recent volcanic action. Many of the lava flows in the Rocky Mountain region are exceedingly youthful. They were poured out during the later periods of earth history which are recorded in the evolution of these mountains. There are many reasons for believing that these mountains are still growing, at an intermittently changing rate. Youthful, vigorous, hardworking streams are trying to lower their channels as rapidly as the mountains rise. We know of streams that have been ponded for a time, because they could not cut downward as rapidly as the mountains rose.

As the crustal portion of the earth yields under pressure and begins to rise, the solid rocks bend or fold, and at places break. Systems of fractures or joints are established, and many cracks may open up. When the mountain mass has reached considerable elevation, changes in temperature from day to night cause the rocks to expand and contract. This weakens the natural cementing materials and causes more cracks to form. If rain collects in such openings, it may freeze and force the sides of the fissures farther apart. Ground waters, especially when charged with humic acids from disintegrating vegetable material, or with carbon dioxide obtained from the air, will dissolve some of the rock particles. This work of solution further weakens the texture of the rock.

Lichens cling to rocks and roughen their surfaces. Seeds of other plants become lodged near the lichens or in cracks. The growth and decay of plants help to form soils. Other seeds are brought by winds or birds. Larger and larger plants take hold, and, as they grow, the roots exert a prying force, which may widen and deepen fissures in the rock. Tree roots can break rocks asunder. All these processes tend to disintegrate even the hardest rock and make it available for agents of transportation.

As rains fall on the land, streams form and begin their work of valley development, sculpturing the earth in their persistent progress, cutting and filling as they sweep onward. Both valleys and mountains pass through stages of youth, maturity, and old age, and the streams, carrying away huge quantities of eroded material and depositing them here and there, contribute to their alteration in a highly substantial degree. The work of no other agent is of equal significance in explaining the relief features in most mountain areas.

At times, when the mountains are exceedingly high, and the climate produces a heavy snowfall, mountain glaciers form in

126

the basins near the summits of the range. These glaciers descend through the canyons, even to the margins of the range. They, too, serve as sculpturing agents, deepening and broadening the canyons through which they move. The story of glaciers among the Rocky Mountains is one of the most fascinating and significant in the history of these ranges.

With the passage of time, and as all the agents of rock disintegration and erosion combine in their efforts, the mountains are slowly carried away. In youth they are rugged and picturesque. Their streams are vigorous and powerful, with rapids and falls in their courses. They are using boulders for tools. As a result, in maturity the ranges are deeply dissected, with many U-shaped valleys and some flat bottom lands, where ranches may be located. Their streams are weaker; they are beginning to meander. They cannot transport weighty rocks, but they roll gravel, pebbles, and even cobblestones, during flood periods, along the beds of their channels. The mountains are slowly being worn down. Their contours are becoming rounded. The Great Smokies and the Friendly Mountains of New England and New York State are in this stage of destruction.

As the work of erosion continues, the valley bottoms become longer and broader, the intervalley ridges lower, and the streams take on the characteristics of old age. They swing lazily in graceful curves through winding channels. At flood times they overflow, shift their channels, and build up natural levees on the bottom lands. Intervalley ridges have been cut by this time into hills, and little by little the hills melt away.

127

After millions of years, the mountain forms have disappeared entirely. A surface of slight relief has been developed. The processes of wearing away and depositing, or degradation and aggradation, have co-operated in the construction of a new landscape, which is so nearly a level plane that it has earned the name "peneplain."

After extreme old age has been reached, very little more can take place until some profound change occurs in the position of this land surface relative to sea level. The streams are down to grade. They cannot cut below sea level. The very old, low hills may be carried away more by solution than by corrosion. Winds may play a part in an old-age topography, for the sands exposed at low-water stages in the river channels may be whirled away to build dunes. Vegetable growth may creep in along the margins of oxbow lakes and other abandoned channels in the flood plains, and help to transform those areas into swamps and finally into dry lands. By this time a cycle of erosion has been completed.

This narrative of Rocky Mountain history is not fiction. It is an account of a well-authenticated sequence of events, which have been duplicated in many other ranges of the world. And it is the most dramatic history we know. It is titanic in theme, this recounting of the birth and death of the everlasting hills! The eternal hills were not eternal, but were leveled by wind, raindrops, and crystals of ice. Today this startling fact is recorded in the flat tops of certain peaks. These flat summits represent an old-age plain, and we call the old-age plain a peneplain. Translated, this means an "almost plane." The plain has been uplifted and eroded until mere

128

remnants remain. There it stands, thousands of feet in the air. But if you sweep your arm so that your fingers trace the accordance of summit levels, you may reconstruct the now uplifted level. The degree of erosion and of the subsequent uplift shocks the imagination and indeed challenges credulity.

CHAPTER SIX

THE ART OF CAMPING

Rocky Mountain columbine, the state flower of Colorado.

Indian squaw grass, or bear grass, in bloom in Glacier National Park.

A short-eared owl.

A ringtailed cat from Montana.

A mountain goat.

A mountain sheep in Wyoming.

WE FOLLOW A TRAIL AND MAKE CAMP

Our trail takes us along a beautiful mountain stream. We stir up deer and in a broad meadow at the margin of a glacial lake catch a glimpse of a huge moose. Small game, birds, and flowering shrubs are abundant in the forested part of our trail. In crossing a high divide we ride for a time along the skyline, with magnificent mountain panoramas on every side. As far as eye can reach, we see one range of snow-capped peaks after another; no two of them are alike; each has its own character and presents its own peculiar puzzle. The cool air of the mountain crest is invigorating, and the trail is just difficult enough to make the ride interesting. No one is thrown, no pack animal missteps and rolls downhill, not a single pack turns. After a perfect day on the trail, a most exhilarating ride, we are now, at dusk, ready to establish a new home.

Many are the joys of the trail, but none compares to the comfort and delight of camp and the end of the day's ride. The healthy fatigue of the trip falls away the moment the tents are raised and the smell of the wood fire fills the grove of aspens or the dense conifers selected for the night's rest. A cool breeze from the heights fills the canyon. There is the friendly sound of the stream. There is happy relief from the saddle. Some lie on the ground, resting, and within scent of the preparing meal. One enthusiast tries for trout in the stream. But all have a contentment that is blessed. The contentment is in sympathy with the horses and pack animals feeding in a meadow.

We have chosen the little opening in the forest on the west side of the canyon, so that the warming influence of the morning sun will strike camp by breakfast time. This means, also, that our camp, in the shadow of the canyon's west wall, will be delightfully cool by evening. The trees about us are magnificent blue spruces and dark-green pines, with a scattering of bright, yellow-green aspens. The color-blends of trees and grasses, the dark mountain walls, and deep-blue sky are fresh and vivid. We are all happy, voices are cheerful, some of the men are whistling, and the work of setting up camp is moving along smoothly. Two or three of the anglers in the party shout back that their luck has been top notch. We'll have trout for supper.

The pack mules and riding horses are soon unsaddled. Although we have picked a place with a good pasture, Arthur Broadhead, our chief packer this year, insists that most of the saddle horses and pack mules must wear hobbles. We are not very far from their corrals, and Arthur, a very careful fellow, fears that the animals may, after getting well filled up with grass, take it into their heads to strike out for home. Most horses and mules seem to have a strong affection for the

134

pastures and barnyards with which they are familiar. Until they become acquainted with one another and accustomed to being together and to our ways of life in the mountains, they are apt to break away.

When plans are all made for a day of field work, and you look forward to some thrilling experience in your scientific studies or to the adventures of a climb to the summit of the mountain range, it is certainly annoying to be told at breakfast time that your favorite saddle horse has not been found. It is especially aggravating if the stock cannot be located early on moving day. Arthur knows this all too well. He has spent many seasons in the mountains with pack outfits, and is not willing to take chances. He is not even satisfied to trust the hobbles, for he has known a hobbled horse to get ten or twelve miles away in a night. Accordingly, he orders that one saddle horse, after grazing two or three hours, be tied near camp and fed grain, so that the wrangler who must round up the stock in the morning will have a handy mount.

As soon as packs are dropped at the end of a moving day, the cook gathers wood and starts his fire. If the weather is good, he prepares his first meal at a new camp over an open fire, while some of us put up his kitchen tent and store away his supplies. The cook is the man who must be kept contented at all costs. Never allow him to be too tired, unhappy, or out of tobacco, or to feel that he is not appreciated. Praise your cook whenever you can, but don't overdo it. Also, take along a few gifts for him, dealing them out as the season progresses. A cook's life is none too easy. Rain! Breaking camp! Searching for firewood! Up early in the morning before the others!

135

The last through at night! A good cook *makes* a trip, a sulky one spoils it.

The packer, too, is a busy man. He has worried about the pack animals through the whole day. He looks cursingly for lost animals in the morning. He has charge of all camp equipment and at night he must cover saddles, blankets, bridles, and ropes with large mantas. He helps to pitch the tents and gathers firewood. Everyone lends a hand, but in a scientific expedition there are notes to be written up, and there are conferences. Vacationists are apt to be thoughtless, or too tired to be of much assistance. Everyone, of course, makes his own bed, either gathering boughs to sleep on or blowing up the air mattresses.

Within an hour the men return with plenty of rainbow and speckled trout for one meal, and we soon hear that most welcome of all camp calls: "Come and get it!" The cook doesn't need to do much urging. After a day in the saddle everyone is ready long before he calls. We gather round the open fireplace where he has been working and help ourselves from the steaming-hot dishes and the big frying pan filled with sizzling trout. Service is on the cafeteria plan. A canvas may have been spread on the ground to serve as a tablecloth, or at least as the center of operations. The scene that follows is picturesque: one sits at the edge of the canvas with legs crossed, tailor fashion, holding his plate between his knees; another reclines, as ancient Romans did, resting on an elbow as he eats from his plate on the ground; some find old stumps or logs where they can sit and hold their plates in their laps. Many campers stand while they eat, especially after their first

136

day in the saddle. If there are children, they may even eat
on the run.

THE CAMPFIRE

To an old-timer there is nothing that symbolizes camp life
in the wilderness more vividly or more pleasantly than the
campfire. There we gather each night and report our discoveries, the interesting incidents of the day, and probably
some ridiculous accidents that have occurred along the trail.
Someone held a tree branch so long that when he let go, it hit
the next man on the trail a stinging blow; or he stirred up a
hornets' nest for the next rider to enjoy. A porcupine
frightened someone's saddle horse. The rider threw his hat
at the little animal and brought home half a hundred quills.
One group saw a mother bear training her two cubs to run at
the scent of man; another discovered sheep high on some
rocky crag; a third narrowly escaped exciting a skunk.

One scientist found an area mantled with huge boulders,
ten to thirty feet in diameter. They could not have been
moved, except by a glacier; and yet they are far away from
the modern valleys, and we are not in a region invaded by the
continental ice sheets. This must mean an early and much
more extensive period of alpine glaciation than that recorded
in the modern canyons. One fellow found escarpments that
indicate great faulting, or slipping. He has located a zone
where the rocks were crushed and recemented with quartz.
There he saw indications of mineralization and a grand opportunity to go prospecting. A geologist discovered the core or

137

vent of an ancient volcano; another reports a section in a canyon where the rock formations are so well exposed that there we may work out the sequence of very ancient geologic events in the range.

As the cooks and packers finish their camp work; they join the party around the fire. If the scientists are still talking shop, they listen most patiently and respectfully, but if we are just entertaining each other, they often join us with western warm-heartedness. Most western men who have lived in the saddle have had interesting experiences. One is an expert in swinging a rope, and he gives us an exhibition equal to anything of its kind at a rodeo show or on a vaudeville stage. Another, who is skilled in making all kinds of knots and in splicing, starts in mending a tie rope which was broken on the trip. That work always interests the boys of a party.

Locating and building a campfire needs careful consideration, especially in a forested area. Indians build them small, and snuggle up close to the blaze. They say: "White man, he build so big fire no one can get near enough to be warm." A medium-sized fire, with logs five to six feet in length, is about right for a small group, and such a fire can be extinguished completely before we all turn in. Most tenderfeet complain of being cold on one side and hot on the other, and do not seem to enjoy a campfire. That trouble is easily overcome by putting up a large piece of canvas, held by posts or a rope, between trees. The heat reflected from the canvas warms the other side. All are soon so comfortable that only the thought of the early morning call can send us to our beds.

One year I engaged as a packer a man named Dan, who

138

was living on a little ranch among the foothills of the San Juan Mountains. He proved to be very familiar with horses and he was an excellent rider. Dan was a silent soul. Not even the glow of good-fellowship inspired by the evening campfire ever loosened his tongue. With everyone else chatting cheerily and freely in the circle about the crackling logs, his persistent mumness was all the more baffling.

Dan had a folding rifle, which he always kept within easy reach, even bringing it to the campfire and putting it in the grass near him. As I think of it now, it is strange we didn't notice that he was extremely nervous, as well as extremely silent.

One day I learned his story. While living in Texas, Dan had been accused of stealing a horse. Powerful influences in the community, including certain local men who may have been guilty of the theft themselves, succeeded in having him convicted of the crime and imprisoned. Dan's friends were enraged. They threatened to break into the jail with a mob and free him. Thereupon, the sheriff decided to transfer Dan to a jail in another town.

He was chained to another prisoner and placed in a closed car, with two guards, one in the front seat, driving, and the other in the rear, near the door. Each guard carried a rifle. When the party reached a desolate stretch of road several miles from town, Dan overpowered the rear guard, seized his rifle, shot the driver, and then shot the other guard. In the scuffle the rear guard fired a revolver several times, and one of the bullets happened to kill the other prisoner. When the smoke cleared, Dan grabbed the wheel, turned the car into a winding wood road, and brought it to a shrieking stop. In the pocket of one of the guards he found a knife, with which he amputated the foot of his dead fellow prisoner at the ankle and thus freed himself.

Over twenty years had passed, but Dan knew he was still being hunted, for the relatives of the men whom he had shot had sworn to get him someday. There was a price on his head, several thousand dollars, in fact. He told me that he never slept soundly, never really relaxed; he was always tense and suspicious, fearful of capture. He was remarkably quick in his actions, like the wild animals in the forest. Quick, because he was being hunted; quick, because he was always on the alert; tense and nervous, just like a lion, or a wolf, or a coyote.

Dan never talked freely or frankly, even in that most encouraging friendliness that grows up about a campfire. He had lost the power of genuine good-fellowship; he was frightened by every strange sound about the camp. He would turn quickly if anyone approached, and he kept close tab on every one of us, so that if any of us ever left the group, he would not be unnecessarily surprised by the rustle of our comings and goings.

Once we asked Dan to enter a little shooting contest, just for sport. I never knew a man who could shoot better. That little folding rifle would come up to his shoulder, and, with scarcely a moment for taking aim, he would hit a spot not larger than a dime at a distance of twenty-five feet without missing once in a dozen trials.

Dan was not trained in any field of science, and the shop talk that occupied a considerable part of our time in camp did

140

not mean much to him. He would listen as a child does to a mystery story. Perhaps he wondered whether we really were able to tell when and how the mountains were made, how they were being destroyed, and why the great mineral deposits were concentrated in certain zones in the mountain structure. If Dan thought we were dreamers, he never showed any disrespect for us. He served loyally and well throughout the field season, but at times he was amused by our enthusiasm. Once, when we were talking of a peneplain as being nearly a plain, he asked if it would be okay to call a swamp a "penelake." I doubt if he ever believed our stories of the glaciers that formerly inhabited the mountain area.

USING HORSE SENSE

Field work in rugged mountain areas has some dangers. You may be hurt, and you may get lost. Reasonable care and good common sense should be used at all times. I have seen plenty of wild game in wilderness regions, but have never been in danger on that account. From my experiences, I think the game animals in our part of the world prefer to avoid trouble.

One season we were in a region with so many bear that we feared we might accidentally surprise and frighten one. My companion and I agreed to take turns whistling, or singing, or in making some kind of an audible noise, when we were crossing through a thicket where a bear might be enjoying a siesta. There is no sense in stirring up unnecessary trouble. Everyone says it is unwise, and I think it is almost impossible to get

141

between a mother bear and her cubs. It is certainly the better part of wisdom to let the grizzlies have a good chance to get away.

In certain parts of the West, we sometimes come across rattlesnakes. We always wear high boots in such territory, so that we are not likely to be struck, and rattlesnakes are usually very accommodating, for they announce their presence in advance. If you see a rattlesnake, there is no need of getting into trouble with him. You can, if you wish, kill him and obtain the rattles as a souvenir. I remember a saddle horse that jumped so suddenly from the trail that he nearly left me behind, when he heard a snake give its warning rattle. Some horses either sense the danger of such snakes, or they just shy at the sound, which is strange to them.

One year I had with me a young man who had never been in the wilderness. We were tramping together, and back-packing; that is, we were each carrying as a back-pack a light bed and a share of the food and cooking utensils necessary for a night or two out in the open. We came to an ice-cold mountain stream, which we had to ford. Since the current was strong and we might be in up to our waists and stepping on boulders, I suggested that we each cut a strong staff and use it for additional support in crossing. I started in first and picked out as good a route as I could, placing my staff before each step squarely on the downstream side, so as to brace me against the force of the current as I lifted one foot. With a pack of forty or fifty pounds on your back, you do not feel very secure in such a situation. It is a good experience to have, for thereafter you will sympathize intelligently with your pack mules, each carrying 200 to 300 pounds, when they are forced to cross mountain torrents. Upon reaching the farther bank safely, I looked around, and there was my companion, helpless in midstream, with his staff on the upstream side. A little horse sense is an asset in our work.

In the more rugged portions of a range, and especially in regions where trails are not shown on the maps, you should never plan to work alone. In climbing to some outlook station, you may slip and turn an ankle, or have a bad fall and break a leg. In crossing a glacier, as I have said before but must warn you of again, the footing may be very uncertain. It is always best to have a companion on such trips.

Your horse may be the cause of an accident. He may be frightened by some wild animal in the forest or by some strange noise and may throw you from the saddle. You cannot give all your attention to a horse and be ready for every emergency. A scientific worker must be constantly on the alert for significant data that must be recorded on his map. He must study his route, keep careful notes as to his location, and be ready to record accurately all important discoveries. On a pleasure trip, you will want to be looking around at the trees, flowers, wild animals, and the distant peaks.

A horse that needs constant attention to keep him from bucking is not the kind of an animal for mountain trips. Some horses become frightened when you unfold a map in the saddle, or click a camera, or turn to put on a slicker in a rainstorm. If thrown, you may be hurt; you may lose your horse and have to return to camp on foot.

When the country is open and trails are well marked so

143

that we can tell each other our general plan for the day, we may separate and visit different regions, but if the trail is lost, or if for any reason you stay out after dark, there will be much concern in camp. You may find, when lost, that your horse, given his head, will pick out the right trail for camp. An experienced mountain horse seems to have a good sense of direction. I remember a favorite saddle horse that I had for many years who, when he hit a new trail, would put his nose near the ground and blow upon the soil and then sniff it, much as a dog will do. He could tell whether other horses of our party had moved over the trail recently, and usually he had enough sense of direction to know which way to go in order to reach camp. When an interesting scent was picked up, he would start off with a bound, and it behooved his rider to be sitting squarely in the saddle and duly alert. At intervals of a few hundred yards he would put his nose down and sniff the trail, even though he was trotting, in order to be sure that he was right.

STAYING OUT OVERNIGHT

If darkness comes on before you have reached camp, and your route lies through a forested area, it is best to stop and wait until morning. Riding through a forested area on a dark night, even on a trail, is very dangerous. A dry bough, or even a twig, may put out an eye, or puncture an ear, or deliver a nasty scratch. A broken tree across the trail, just high enough to let your horse pass, may strike you across the breast or in

144

the face and knock you off the saddle. The horse may be frightened and, if your feet do not come free from the stirrups, you will be dragged—and perhaps for the last time. Rather than take chances on a trail through a forest in the dark, I have stopped more than once with my saddle horse and stayed out overnight.

An unexpected night in the open is a rather interesting experience and gives plenty of time for meditation. You know you are causing your companions trouble, but you figure that in the end it will be better for you to arrive in your saddle than on a stretcher. If your horse is an old-timer, he will sense the situation. You should first unsaddle him and allow him to graze. Build a little fire for yourself, arrange your riding saddle as a headrest, and make yourself as comfortable as possible until the supper hour has passed. Then you will feel better.

Your saddle horse should be watched very carefully when you spend the night out. He may think he knows the way back to camp and decide to leave you. I remember one that was so companionable that he would stay close to me and, after grazing for two or three hours, would lie down near the campfire. Once I snuggled up near his back and used his body as a windbreak. With the fire on one side of me and the horse on the other, I was reasonably comfortable for a time. He stayed with me for three or four hours, and then got up and went grazing again. I kept close watch on him, for even though he was very friendly and sociable, I knew that he wanted to get back to the other horses. As soon as the morning

145

light began to brighten up the landscape the least bit, he thought it was time to move, so I saddled up, and we were off. We reached camp just in time for breakfast.

I recall the instance of an eminent geologist of our National Survey, Dr. Whitman Cross, my associate for many summer seasons in mountain camps. He once found himself, toward the end of the day, trying to get through a windfall of timber, where there had been a forest fire. The fallen timber had made an almost impassable tangle. The logs in such a mess cross each other at various angles and point up and down and in every possible direction. Just drop a handful of wooden matches or toothpicks on a table, and you will produce in miniature such a formation.

Dr. Cross kept thinking he could find a way through this jungle and get into camp in time for supper. He pushed on farther and farther, turning first in one direction and then in another, jumping some obstacles, moving others, and trying as best he could to find a way for himself and his saddle horse. Many a time he dismounted and climbed over a log, and then forced his horse to jump. The sun was setting and darkness was coming on. He had gone too far to turn back, or to try a different route to camp, so he decided to stay out for the night. Tying his horse to a tree trunk, he made a little windbreak for himself. A campfire would have been a real comfort, but in a pile of crisp, dry kindling wood, that was unsafe. If he made a fire and accidentally went to sleep and a strong wind came up, there might be serious trouble. True, he might have scrambled over the logs and gotten away, but his horse and

146

outfit might have been lost. It was a dry season. Dr. Cross decided against taking a chance with a fire and, consequently, he did not have a very comfortable night.

Of course, we missed him. Any member of a party who is very late getting in causes worry. We offer all kinds of reasons. Some think the man has had an accident. He may have fallen from his horse; he may have slipped and turned an ankle and be unable to remount. Some think we should go out and search for him. Others insist that he is probably all right, that he is such an enthusiastic mountain explorer that he forgets all about time and doesn't start back to camp until it is too late to get in before dark. Some say he has been out overnight several times, for he is a kind of night bird. One of us decides to fire a gun at intervals to give him a signal of the camp's location. We all feel a little ashamed of ourselves for not starting a search—but where are we to go, what trail are we to follow? There are a dozen possible routes into camp. If a man has been out all day with a horse, there is a wide range of country where he might have had a mishap. Shall we start out through a forest in the darkness? All of us who are trained to live in the open know this is very dangerous and very slow. If the missing man does not appear for breakfast or soon after, we will abandon all other plans and set out in search of him. Fortunately, Dr. Cross arrived just in time for bacon and eggs, safe and sound, and relieved the strain on our consciences.

After twenty-five field seasons in wilderness areas, with scores of men of varying experience living in camp with me,

147

I have never had a serious mishap, and I have had but one man lost for as long as three days. Old-timers are practically certain to get in for breakfast.

ONE MAN GETS LOST

The man who was lost for three days was one of a group of eastern college students in the western mountains for the first time. He and his companion, working on foot, were supposed to remain together. They had been given definite instructions never to separate when far away from camp. Yet one of them arrived at camp rather late one evening, alone, with the explanation that his companion had insisted on taking a trail that led directly away from camp.

The lost man, Prescott, was without food; and, knowing his limited experience, we set out immediately to find him. We were camped near the tree line in the Wind River Range, where most of the trails were over meadowlands or bare rock areas, and the going was not as dangerous as in a densely forested region. The searching parties all returned to the spot where the two men had separated. There we called, shot off guns, built a fire on a hilltop that could be seen for miles in several directions, and did everything else we could think of to help Prescott locate us. Then, some of us went off on different trails and kept up our efforts to get in touch with the lost pardner. All was in vain; and about midnight the searching parties returned to camp. During the next two days, horsemen scoured the country in an endeavor to find our lost companion, but to no avail. A third night went by. We decided he had

148

selected a stream course and started for the low country, hoping to strike some ranch home. On the third day after Prescott disappeared, it was necessary to move camp, and late in the afternoon, just as the party was passing through a little rocky col high among the mountains, we saw our lost companion resting before us in a beautiful alpine garden on the sunny side of the range. He was about fifteen miles from our old camp. We were completely surprised, for we had given up all hope of finding him in the mountains. He seemed unconcerned and not in the least worried, but did not want to talk about his adventure. We gave him a little food, had him mount a saddle horse and fall into line. Not until he had eaten a good supper and we were gathered round our evening campfire did we learn much from him. He had spent fairly comfortable nights near little campfires. A bar of chocolate, which he happened to have in his pocket, helped to sustain his strength during the first day out. Berries and plenty of good mountain water had made up the rest of his diet. Prescott had wandered about, but had no idea of the direction of the camp site; all he knew was that it was near the tree line, and for that reason he had stayed high in the mountains. He said he had planned before long to follow a stream and thus get out of the mountains.

There is no better way to know people well than to live with them in a wilderness region for a month or two. The hardships and emergencies incurred test health, strength, self-reliance, character, and good-fellowship. Plenty of critical situations arise while traveling through a mountain area with a pack train, and the many evenings spent about campfires, exchanging ideas on all kinds of topics and telling stories, help us to get acquainted. Before the season is over, each member of the little group is sure to have had ample opportunity to tell of his or her special adventures. Those evenings of comradeship are never forgotten, and we become, as a rule, lifelong friends.

The art of camping is to make one's self and one's companions comfortable. It is a mistake to travel too light and to forgo essentials. The experienced camper has learned to leave useless gadgets at home but, on the other hand to take full equipment of necessities and to be prepared for changes of weather. It is not only physical weather, but human temper, that changes. In camp, making others comfortable is of first importance. If you are tired, others are also, especially any children that may be along. A long trail and making camp is a test for the best of us.

CHAPTER SEVEN

MOUNTAINS ARE WORN AWAY

One of the most remarkable aspects of Rocky Mountain scenery is the frequent evenness in its sky line. Mile after mile, as far as one can see, the summits come to approximately the same elevation. Broad areas, high in the ranges but a little below the isolated crest-line peaks, correspond so closely in elevation that in imagination they might be conceived of as remnants of a continuous surface.

The summit of the Rampart Range in Colorado is so gently rolling that the farmers use the land for planting grain. Pikes Peak rises as a conspicuous elevation above this summit area. In the San Juans, there are large surfaces a little below the highest peaks that are at about an equal elevation. If we could, in imagination, fill the modern canyons to their rims, a broad, gently rolling plain would be reproduced, much as it looked before the streams began cutting the modern canyons. For many years we called this imaginary erosion surface the San Juan Peneplain. We knew it had existed and we knew it must have been developed by the work of streams in an earlier cycle of erosion. When this surface was formed as a gently rolling plain, it must have been 4,000 to 5,000 feet lower in altitude than it is today, for it was as low as the streams of that day could cut their channels.

Following this period, when streams flowed lazily over a more or less level plain, came a renewal of mountain growth, a redoming of the area, and a rejuvenation of all the streams. The invigorated streams began at once to lower their channels and thus to dissect the subsummit plain. As the valleys became deeper, isolated areas of the old plain were left high above the river courses.

Every area exposed to stream erosion must eventually be leveled to a plain which slopes gently to the sea. On this almost level plain the sluggish (old-age) streams barely make their way, so gentle is their gradient. There will be occasional hills left, topping above the general level, for which we have adopted the Indian name, monadnocks. Thus, Pikes Peak is apparently a monadnock above the plain now marked by the accordance of summit levels of the Rampart Range. This plain never reaches the theoretical base level. It is an "almost base-level" plain. It is the history of peneplains that in course of time they are uplifted and worn away. The theory is that the flat-topped mountains and the accordance of summit levels in the Rockies represent an eroded and uplifted peneplain.

Over and over again among the different ranges of the Rockies we have found remnants of a peneplain a little below the highest summits. The one in the Medicine Bow Range in Wyoming is particularly striking, with the Snowy Range of that area rising above it, just as Pikes Peak, in the Front Range of Colorado, rises above a similar surface.

154

The Wind River Range furnishes striking evidence of great erosion in the development of a peneplain surface a few hundred feet below the summit. In some areas the very ancient core rocks are beveled to the peneplain level; in others, sedimentary layers are cut to that level. To the uninitiated, the sight of upturned layers of sedimentary rocks, such as limestones, sandstones, and shales, beveled off to an even surface of almost prairie flatness, seems nothing short of bewildering. Every observant person pauses and asks for an explanation of how the apparently impossible has been accomplished. I have heard lawyers, doctors, ranchmen, college students and all manner of men wonder how those rocks, now high in the mountains, could have been upturned, and how and why they were cut off so evenly. The story of the folding, of long erosion, and of uplift is right before us—a great outdoor diagram.

These discoveries, made in one range after another as our work advanced and by others who were examining various parts of the Rocky Mountain region, have resulted in the accumulation of a great mass of data bearing on the erosion history of the Rockies. We are now convinced that in the late history of the mountain area, just before the last great period of growth or uplift, there must have been a very widespread plain where now we have so many different ranges. We call that ancient surface the Rocky Mountain Peneplain. Parts of this old surface have been recognized in the Sawatch and Mosquito Ranges, and in Green Ridge, north of Rocky Mountain National Park in Colorado; in the Laramie, Big Horn, and Owl Creek Ranges of Wyoming; in the Uinta Mountains of Utah, and at various other places in the mountain areas of western Montana and eastern Idaho.

Recognition of this ancient peneplain is not based solely upon uniformity of level, or upon the truncation of structures. At several localities we have found water-worn gravels which represent the work of old-age streams that once wandered about on its surface. These gravels, which were deposited in stream channels, are now thousands of feet above the beds of the modern near-by streams. They record a late stage of an earlier cycle of erosion.

The Rocky Mountain Peneplain, as identified, is an important key to the interpretation of the history of each range where it is represented. No one knows how otherwise to account for broad expanses now high above the stream channels, where the geologic structures have been truncated, where old-age valleys may be present, and where the stream deposits of old-age rivers remain, than by the story of the development of a peneplain and the subsequent uplift of that surface. As soon as uplift occurred, streams were quickened and began to dissect the old-age surface. A new cycle of erosion began. All ancient peneplains, therefore, are today partially dissected, and their recognition may not be too easy a task, even for an experienced fieldworker.

FILLING THE BASINS AND MAKING A PLAIN

While the mountains were being worn down and the great Rocky Mountain Peneplain was being developed, the rock material taken from those mountain areas was accumulating

156

on the neighboring lowlands. This process of building up the lower lands to the east and west, and in the basins or parks between the ranges, is just as important and as significant as the work of erosion. The two processes, degradation and aggradation, went on simultaneously.

In time the processes of filling built up the lower areas to about the same elevation as the worn-down, or peneplaned, areas of the mountains. Alluvial or waste material actually mantled large portions of the peneplain. At this stage the relief in the Rocky Mountain province was comparatively slight. Certainly the relief then was much less than that of today. Some higher crest-line peaks rose above the peneplaned areas as monadnocks, just as Mt. Monadnock, in New Hampshire, rises above a conspicuous peneplain in the Friendly Mountains of New England. The gently rolling surface of that day was made up in part of areas reduced by erosion, and in part of a vast expanse of territory at about the same elevation, built up by the depositing of sands, gravels, and silts brought from the mountains.

In the lowlands and in the basins between the main ranges, hills and low mountain forms were completely buried. The thickness of sediments which accumulated during this period amounted at places to at least 6,000 feet. Some considerable mountain areas, such as the Granite Range of central Wyoming, were completely buried.

The outwash silts and gravels of this basin-filling period spread hundreds of miles east of the Rockies over the surface of the Great Plains. They remain today at places on the High Plains of our Middle West. Similar wash spread southward

157

into New Mexico and westward over the surface of the Colorado Plateau. Some of those gravels are now present on the surface of Mesa Verde, southwest of the San Juans in Colorado, and at an elevation of about 7,800 feet above the sea. That famous mesa has been isolated by later erosion, but it was once a part of the widespread surface developed by erosion and filling just before the last great mountain-making period of the West.

As the filling of the basins advanced, the sands and gravels became more widely distributed. Many of the major ranges of today were partially covered with these loose materials. On the slopes of the Uinta Range, 9,000 to 10,000 feet above sea level, there remain to this day vast amounts of this gravel outwash. Other remnants of such deposits have been discovered on peneplain surfaces in the San Juan Mountains at elevations 12,000 feet above sea level, and in the Rampart, Park, and Owl Creek Ranges. These are indeed remarkable discoveries. Think for a moment! Why otherwise should loose stream-borne gravels be so high above sea level, on the tops of some mountain ranges, on the tops of high tablelands, and thousands of feet above the stream beds where such gravels are being worked over today?

The history sketched thus far requires imagination. It is built upon significant data picked up, little by little, here and there in the mountain region. Still ahead of us, awaiting consideration in the story of the Rocky Mountains, are the more recent events in mountain chronology which have produced the scenic features of today; but, just as in the human record, all becomes clear once the historic background has been established. If the physical evolution of the Rocky Mountains closed at this stage, we should have nothing within their compass worth going very far to see. The landscape would present a gently rolling plain, with a few low hills and mountains scattered widely throughout the region. The Rockies would not have been a barrier to travel and transportation as settlers pushed westward. They would not have cut off the rain-bearing winds from the west and caused, as they do today, the Great Plains to be a semiarid belt, where dust bowls develop. Many of the rich ores of the region would never have been discovered. There would be no lakes, no great waterfalls, and few rapids or cascades. The glaciers, which we have yet to tell about, would not have formed in this part of the country. There would be no beauty spots demanding preservation as national parks. There would be but few forested areas, and those would be small. The renewal of uplift, the erection of the great rock barrier, the rebirth of the mountains when they were lifted to elevations somewhat higher than today, the quickening of all streams, the formation of glaciers, the work of the ice; all this has come since the development of the widespread surface of erosion and filling which has been described. We have the magnificent scenic features in the Rockies because they are young. They have been reborn, reuplifted, and now they exhibit all the characteristics of youth.

CHAPTER EIGHT

A DAY IN THE WIND RIVER MOUNTAINS

4:00 A.M.—The crackling of the cook's fire.

4:30 A.M.—The horse wranglers leave to round up the stock.

5:30 A.M.—Everybody is called.

6:00 A.M.—"Come and get it or I'll throw it out!"

9:00 A.M.—We hit the trail.

11:00 A.M.—We pass Square Top and Green River Lakes.

1:00 P.M.—Lunch on a sky-line divide.

2:00-6:00 P.M.—Without a trail and some rough going.

6:00 P.M.—Al finds a possible route.

7:30 P.M.—We establish a camp near Simpson Lake.

10:00 P.M.—Al tells us a bedtime story.

Floyd, our cook, and his assistant have been up for fully two hours; after bringing in the stock, the horse wranglers have been fed, and it is time everyone was ready for breakfast. Floyd gives us the final call: "Come and get it or I'll throw it out." Moans and groans are heard from several directions, for there are a number of young people who are new campers in the party, but nevertheless one after another appears, washes in the ice-cold water of a mountain stream near our camp, picks up a cup, plate, knife, fork, and spoon, and waits for his turn to secure a hot flapjack, a bowl of mush, some bacon and eggs, and a cup of coffee.

In a rope corral, improvised near the camp, Al, Pete, and Buck are hard at work roping one animal after another and saddling them expertly as they waltz in circles. Al is the outfitter and head packer; Pete and Buck are his assistants. There are seventeen riding saddles to be carefully placed and twenty-two packsaddles to be cinched. Each animal fights for his lib-

163

erty, dodging the great loop in the swinging rope as long as he can.

"What shall we do about the mountain climbers, Doctor?" calls out Al. "They were due in yesterday afternoon. I had a man up the canyon with saddle horses waiting for them until dark last night. They didn't come in, and they aren't in yet." Three of the men had gone off to climb Gannett and evidently had been delayed.

"If they don't show up before the pack train is ready to move, leave a man with their saddle horses and one pack animal camped on the trail for them. He can wait until late in the afternoon and then push on and catch up with us before dark. If they are very late, or unable to travel, have them stay at the dude ranch, three miles down the valley, and catch up with us tomorrow. Be sure you contact them before the end of the day."

By ten o'clock the party is mounted and starts down the canyon on a good trail. They pass the beautiful lakes of Green River, pass the dude ranch where eastern city people come to wear chaps and spurs and ride out over the near-by hills with dude camp cowboys dressed in brilliant red or yellow shirts, twenty-dollar sombreros, and twenty-dollar high-heeled boots. These picturesque fellows entertain the eastern dudes during the summer seasons. They carry lariat ropes on their saddles, and some have learned to throw them over posts about the camp with great skill, but they never use them in the saddle, for they need both hands to "pull leather" when their horses go very fast.

This is a magnificent mountain country, with lofty snow-

164

covered peaks, beautiful lakes, forests, streams that teem with trout, and some big game. We catch glimpses of deer, elk, mountain sheep, and occasionally a bear. It is still a wilderness. Though shepherds bring their flocks into the alpine pastures of the Wind Rivers during the summer, they and a few vacationists are all that you may see, even if you travel from one end of the range to the other. It is not a richly mineralized range, and therefore it is without mining camps.

During the open season big-game hunting is done in the Wind Rivers. The dude ranches are visited in the fall of the year by a variety of bold Americans who engage hardy natives of Wyoming, real western cowmen who know the hills, to take them out, find the game, and tell them when, where, and how to shoot. Al told us all about it. "We charge these sports a good fee for each day's service, and the State requires a hunting license." After many fruitless efforts to be calm and shoot well, these indoor-target-practice experts return home with glorious accounts of their hunting experiences. Seldom does any one of them admit that his guide shot simultaneously with him when he actually took the game.

A short distance below the ranch the trail turns into the hills and crosses into the valley of Roaring Fork. Slowly we climb out of the canyon of Green River and push on over the divide into the next valley. Here, according to our map, the trail makes a turn into the valley before mounting the far wall, but there is no sign of such a bend. As we hunt for some hint or trace of it, the pack train comes into sight. The packs are light, for we have been out over three weeks, and most of the provisions have been consumed. The animals come at a trot into the bottom lands of Roaring Fork, with Floyd guiding them down-valley and then to the summit on the north. Floyd says he knows the location of an old trail.

Most of the riders take a short-cut route up the hill, and, to their surprise and great gratification, stir up a herd of about twenty young elk. Eugene, our artist and movie fan, is called to the front, and with his characteristic energy exerted on the bulging sides of his poky old horse, succeeds in getting into a good position and in exposing a few feet of film on the elk just as they are disappearing into a forest.

At the crest of the north wall of Roaring Fork valley we all pause and dismount. The trail we were following has played out. During lunch we hold a conclave and decide to follow the mountain crest eastward to a pass just above Simpson Lake, and then descend and set up camp on its shores.

The route for two or three miles is over a rolling grassland; there is no trail, but the going is easy, and the mountain vistas are magnificent. We are at an elevation of about 10,000 feet above the sea. To the east and southeast are the high peaks of the Wind River Range—Fremont, Gannett, and many others —which we had lived near for many happy days. To the southwest are the bare summits of the Gros Ventre Range, and far to the west rise the majestic spires of the mighty Tetons. The region of the Yellowstone to the northwest is overhung with a gray cloud of smoke, which reports a forest fire raging in that section of the country. We are on the top of the range and can see far off in every direction. A sky-line trail in a high mountain area is a most exhilarating route to follow in the saddle and we are all in the best of spirits.

On and on we ride, getting higher and higher, when suddenly Floyd tells us we must drop down again into Roaring Fork canyon and proceed up a narrow gorge to a certain pass. We cannot follow the sky line of the mountains any farther. The descent is terrible. It is so steep and rocky that many of the pack animals refuse to go on. They mill round and round at the crest of a precipitous slope over which Al is coaxing them to move. Then suddenly something breaks loose. The animals realize they have a different type of man behind them. Al has lost patience, and he lets go with both lariat and voice: "Get to hell out of here, you rabbit-eared cayuses. What did I feed you grain all winter for; can't you do a day's work? Get up on your feet, you good-for-nothing middle-sexed neutrals, or I'll leave you here to rot." The pack animals begin jumping, falling, rolling, and scrambling to the base of the hill— and Al is right behind them.

On and on we push our tired horses. The usual time for making camp passes. It is five o'clock, and for many places in the canyons the sun has set. Night is fast approaching, and yet we are on the wrong side of the mountain range, and miles from Simpson Lake. A yell from Al directs us upward. He thinks he has discovered the pass. After another hour of heavy trail work we all reach the summit and look over. Before us is a vertical drop of several thousand feet. At the base there is a pile of rough angular talus. There is no place to ride or walk. We are in a perfectly impossible situation. Finally, Al decides that we had better descend and look for another pass. This time he finds a route through the mountain crest, and we start down the northern slope of the range.

As darkness closes in on our overworked outfit, camp is set up on the shores of Simpson Lake. The long-sought goal has been reached. Everyone is tired, dusty, and very hungry. It is a difficult task to prepare supper in the dark for seventeen people, and Floyd is just as tired as anyone in the party, but he has been most to blame for our long detours, and he makes no complaints. By ten in the evening supper is over, the horses are all feeding in a near-by meadow, most of the beds for the party have been made up for the night, and we are happily resting about the campfire, when a fearful wheezing and blowing sound is heard. At first we think it is Eugene, who has lagged far behind the party all through the ride. Searchlights are at once turned in the direction of the sound, revealing, of all things, the amiable and jovial face of our guardian angel and guide, all puffed out, in a mighty endeavor to inflate his mattress.

"If any of you are as tired as I am, you'll want to go to bed, too. I call this a hard day's work."

"Oh, Al, tell us a story and then we'll all go to bed."

"All right," said Al, "and it'll be a darned good one, too. One day some years ago I was a-riding in these here hills. We were all alone, my horse and I, and we had climbed up a terrible steep slope, when all of a sudden that horse of mine whirled, headed down the slope, and began to buck for all he was worth. And boy, can that horse buck! Each time I went up in the air I lost sight of the animal completely. But I held on. All I was afraid of was what he would do when he reached that big fallen tree I'd made him jump as we came up the mountain. Down the hill we went. I saw the big tree coming

168

nearer and nearer. I went high into the air, but I was all right, until the ground got in my way. Then everything went blank. The next thing I recollect, the horse and I were lying together near the bottom of the hill. When I picked myself up, there was a terrific pain in my chest, and two of my ribs were sticking right through my shirt front. I pushed the ribs back into place and hurried to look at my horse. One front leg was broken, and the bone came clean through, several inches beyond that animal's hide. The right rear leg was broke too, and one hoof was just hanging by a thin cord. I went straight to work on him, made some splints from a flexible slippery elm at hand, grabbed the adhesive tape—I always carry a roll of the stuff—and fixed up all the bones, geared up new joints in the broken legs—and that was all there was to it. We turned around and headed for home. That'll give you an idea why Eugene is having a little trouble keeping up with the party. He's riding that same horse today. Good night, pals, we've had a great day in the mountains."

CHAPTER NINE

MOUNTAINS RISE AGAIN

Millions of years after the birth of the Rocky Mountains, after billions of tons of rock material had been removed from the ranges and deposited in the neighboring lower lands, after the great Rocky Mountain Peneplain had been developed by erosion and the even more extensive surface due to filling or deposition had been produced, a renewal of uplift and mountain growth occurred. This was a physical revolution of major significance and was very widespread. It occurred in late Tertiary time, or just before the opening of the last Great Ice Age in the Pleistocene period of earth history. It was the last widespread mountain-making period in North America.

If you ask why this movement took place and why at this particular time, one can only answer with theories. We know that the force of gravity, drawing everything toward the center of the earth, must set up stresses and strains in the rock material of this planet. The rigidity of the crustal portion of the earth will withstand these stresses and strains for a time,

173

but if that is overcome, something will give, and there will be movement. Each movement to relieve the strains may be but two or three feet, and human beings within its range then speak of earth tremor. If it occurs suddenly, they speak of terrain earthquakes. If such movements continue, something like mountain growth will be taking place. Some think that the unloading of certain areas by erosion and the loading of other places with sediments may be a cause of movement in the outer, or crustal, part of the earth. The heavier places tend to settle, pushing like wedges against less resistant portions of the earth crust, and forcing these lighter parts to rise.

One theory holds that the continental masses and the rocks beneath the continents are lighter than the masses of rock below the oceans. If so, the great wedge-shaped masses of the earth beneath the oceans, as they are drawn toward the center of the earth, must push against the lighter continental wedges. The fact that the edges of the continents are wrinkled or folded at so many places is cited in support of this theory.

The great thrust faulting which we have described in the Rocky Mountains and similar faulting in other parts of the earth are away from the oceans. This indicates that the pressure came from the direction of the ocean floor.

Even if we do not know why such movements occurred, or why they came just when they did, we do know that there have been several such great physical revolutions during the latter part of the earth history.

Geologists commonly divide the known history of the earth

into eras, and the closing of one era and the opening of another are placed at a time when there was some great physical revolution similar to the one we are now dealing with in the history of the Rocky Mountains.

While the Rocky Mountain area was being uplifted, the bordering areas of great plains to the east and high plateaus to the west were elevated. In fact, most of the far-western portion of North America was affected. As the movement continued, old lines of folding and faulting were re-emphasized, and the mountain ranges were uplifted more than the basin areas. Thus, the major relief features in the modern landscape were redefined.

The story from here on is one of continued uplift in the mountain areas and continued earth sculpturing. The uplifted land became subject to a renewal of stream cutting. Every stream that acquired a steeper gradient quickened its rate of cutting. Each major river began to lower its channel toward the new base level of erosion, the level below which streams cannot cut. At first, the new valleys were sharp V-shaped notches characteristic of youth, but as time passed, the valleys became deeper and wider. The major streams and many of their tributaries meanwhile cut the gorges into the deep, picturesque mountain canyons of today.

Before the work of stream erosion had advanced very far, glaciers formed in the mountains and assisted in deepening and widening all of the valleys through which they passed, but the first hacking and hewing in the job of sculpture was done by streams. Their action, following the opening of the last

175

great physical revolution, supplies one of the most fascinating and significant chapters in the history of the Rockies.

THE CANYON-CUTTING PERIOD

With the uplift in the Rocky Mountain area and the quickening of all major rivers, the deepening of valleys began. This appeared first in the lower, or downstream, sections of the stream courses as the mountains slowly rose. As the obstructions in those portions were removed, the deepening continued farther and farther headward. No tributary could quicken its flow and begin to lower its stream bed until the deepening of the main valley had advanced upstream beyond the mouth of the tributary. Thousands, perhaps millions, of years passed, before the rejuvenated Colorado River, working headward through the great plateau section, carved out the Grand Canyon in Arizona and finally affected the work of its tributaries in the southwestern portion of the mountain province. A long period passed before the quickening of the Arkansas, South Platte, North Platte, Laramie, Sweetwater, Missouri, Yellowstone, and Snake Rivers developed valleys within the Rocky Mountain province.

When the rejuvenating influence finally reached the mountain area, the old-age rivers which were lazily wandering over a nearly level surface took on the characteristics of youth and cut through the alluvial filling into the hard rocks of the mountains. Virtually all the streams were flowing, at places, over buried mountain ranges. Those streams which were located on bare, peneplain surfaces experienced cutting diffi-

176

culties. They found it necessary to attack at once the ancient core-rock formations, and in nearly every instance they cut magnificent water gaps which, today, are among the most out-standing scenic features in the mountain area.

There is not a single major river leaving the Rocky Moun-tain region in the United States today that does not plunge through a mountain range. Several of the master streams have cut canyons in two or more ranges. There are at least twenty-five notable water gaps in the middle and southern portions of the Rocky Mountains within the United States, most of them true examples of streams that have cut through a mantle of loose material deep into the underlying mountain structures.

It is impossible to account for the present river courses by normal headward erosion, for normal streams would have avoided the mountain areas in locating their channels. In time, tributary streams would have worked headward into the mountains. None of them would have chosen to cut through a mountain range if they could have found easy going only a short distance to one side or the other. It is extremely unlikely that they would have cut canyons such as now notch the various ranges within the Rocky Mountain province. The major lines of the present drainage pattern are inherited from the streams which existed on the surface that had been developed by cut-ting down ancient mountains and filling the basins.

THE GREAT GORGES

Therefore, the transmontane gorges tell a great story of the fierce contest that raged between the earth forces of uplift and

177

the atmospheric forces of erosion. Fourteen great canyons cross the mountains, cut by streams whose life history is older than the period of mountain uplift. These canyons, worthy of a visit for their beauty, are important also for any who would read geologic history. The Black Canyon of the Gunnison, on the northern margins of the San Juan Mountains, is one such gorge. Another, also exposing the granite core rock, is cut by the North Platte in the Medicine Bow Range. Apparently, the North Platte established its course when the area between the Medicine Bow and the Park Ranges was filled with wash from the mountains. As the stream lowered its channel, it was forced to cut into the granite barrier previously hidden by soft sediments. Such incidents in river history are all in the nature of special events. They are not the commonplace records of stream erosion.

Southwest of Alcova, Wyoming, the North Platte River flows for several miles through another magnificent gorge cut into ancient granite and upturned rock formations. Before the modern valley was developed, sediments from near-by mountains covered the area, and only a few subdued mountain summits rose above the surface of the waste-filled basin. When uplift occurred, cutting was inaugurated, and the North Platte lowered its course into buried mountain structures. With the varied structure and many-hued rocks, the gorge is a picturesque sight, a natural haunt for those who live in that part of the country.

West of Cheyenne, sediments of the Great Plains lap up on the Laramie Range so that the transition from plain to mountain is almost imperceptible. There is no pronounced

178

change or break in topography. This area, where the old Pony Express route was laid out, and where now the Union Pacific railroad and a modern highway are located, has been appropriately called the "Gangplank." It serves as an easy route from the Great Plains to the summit of one of the mountain ranges.

Approximately forty miles north of the Sherman Mountain area, west of Cheyenne, the Laramie River crosses the Laramie Range. The stream flows from the Laramie Basin, where it has cut a broad, open valley in comparatively soft sediments, directly across the range in a granite gorge, and then enters another broad, open valley cut in the soft rocks of the Great Plains.

Rising at the northern end of the Wind River Range, the Green River flows southward through the Wyoming Basin and plunges directly into the Uinta Range within a few miles of the present village of Manila. There it has cut a canyon, nearly 2,000 feet in depth, through highly-colored sediments that account for the local name, Flaming Gorge. The stream then flows eastward in a canyon, until it reaches Browns Park. Near the center of the park, the stream turns directly south and flows through what is known as Ladore Canyon.

South of the Teton Range, the Snake and the Hoback Rivers unite, then flowing together, as the Snake River, through a canyon with beautifully forested walls. After leaving the soft deposits at the eastern margin of the area, the Hoback River cuts through upturned layers of hard rock. From the village of Hoback, southward and then westward, the Snake River courses in the bed of a mountain canyon for nearly fifteen

179

miles. Here is another example of streams rising in the midst of the Rocky Mountain region and crossing huge mountain ranges in their routes to the sea. At an earlier stage, when the topography was entirely different from that of today, and at a time when there was little or no relief, the streams must have been located in this portion of the province. The streams cut these great gorges as the country was uplifted. They could not avoid these tasks. They had to lower their channels through the rock material that was beneath them.

Among the water gaps of the Rocky Mountain region is the one cut through the Owl Creek Mountains, south of Thermopolis, another instance of a stream's having excavated a gorge directly across a mountain belt. The scenic canyon west of Cody, on the way to the eastern entrance to Yellowstone National Park, has been developed by the Shoshone River, where it cuts through a spur of the Absaroka Range.

The Sweetwater River, a tributary of the North Platte, winds in and out among the remnants of the Granite Range of central Wyoming. A short distance west of historic Independence Rock, where the Mormons passed on their westward trek, it plunges through a picturesque little gorge known as Devils Gate. The land in the vicinity of this miniature canyon is mantled with wash from the mountains. The strange situation of the Sweetwater River can be readily explained, if we imagine the stream flowing on an old surface higher than the top of the gateway and lowering its channel during a new cycle of erosion.

Where the Arkansas River crosses the Colorado Front Range, it has been forced to cut a sharp V-shaped gorge, in some places nearly 2,000 feet deep, in the most ancient core-rock complex. West of the Front Range, near Salida, the stream flows in a broad, intermontane lowland, where there are vast alluvial deposits; then, turning eastward, it plunges into a canyon, which it follows for several miles. The Arkansas River probably flowed on that old erosion surface, lowering its course as the range was uplifted. As the stream has deepened the canyon, there has been a constant struggle to keep pace with the upward growth of the mountains. Whenever mountain growth exceeded the rate of downward cutting, ponding occurred on the west side of the mountains.

Near the eastern margin of the Big Horn Basin, there is the beautifully symmetrical mountain fold through which the Big Horn River has cut a small canyon. A few miles farther north, the stream leaves the basin region and plunges directly into, and through, the Big Horn Range. In order to account for the position of the master stream, one must imagine a mantle of material spread over this entire region and reaching to the summit of the Big Horn Mountains. When this condition existed, the Big Horn River could have established its course across the range. Like the North Platte, Sweetwater, Green, and Shoshone Rivers, the Big Horn is an example of a stream that was flowing over a buried mountain range. As uplift took place, the river quickened its work and lowered its channel into the mountain mass.

Each of the major canyons in the Rocky Mountains, like each of the ranges, has a special story to tell. The erosion or sculpturing of the mountain masses since the last great uplift is still going on. The streams are vigorous. There are falls,

181

rapids, and cascades, which are indications that the streams are not yet down to the grade below which they cannot cut. The whole mountain landscape is in one of its most picturesque stages.

The mountain-making movements probably are still going on. Since the streams are cutting vigorously, the mountains may be rising as fast as, or faster than, the streams can lower their channels. This is known to have happened in the past; it may be true today. Certainly the work of rock-sculpturing in the mountains is but partially done. Millions of years will elapse before these great mountains are worn away and another broad plain is produced in the region where we now have the Rocky Mountains of the United States and Canada.

CHAPTER TEN

THE LAST GREAT ICE AGE

While the great transmontane canyons were being cut down across the rising ranges, a profound change took place over the whole of North America. The continent became colder. Storminess increased. Snows fell in great abundance. So much snow fell in the winters that the weakened sunshine of summer was unable to waste it away. Year by year the accumulation grew greater. Perennial snow fields blanketed the mountains and, in the north, even the lowlands were covered. Under weight and great pressure over a long period, the deep snow was compressed into ice. At first, it was a granular ice, but, as the pressure increased, some melting took place, and the water filling the intergranular spaces froze. Thus the basal portion of each great snowbank became a clear, solid mass of ice which, when thick enough, caused enough pressure to produce movement. In this way great glaciers were formed.

The huge ice sheets which existed in the northeastern part of this continent do not concern us here. The Friendly Mountains of New England and New York State, which rise to 6,000 feet above the sea, were overridden by ice from the centers in eastern Canada. Most of Canada and much of the north-central part of the United States were covered by ice. In the Interior Plateau of British Columbia, a great mass of ice was confined between the Rocky Mountains on the east and the Coast ranges on the west. When this ice mass reached sufficient height, it moved both northward and southward. The southward-moving mass advanced into the territory now included in the states of Montana, Idaho, and Washington, crossed the present valley of the Columbia, and pushed on, even beyond the site of the city of Spokane. That ice gouged out the deep basins in which the long valley lakes of Canada are now located.

While the great ice sheets of North America were forming, snows were accumulating in each of the high mountain areas in the cordilleran portion of the continent. The snows became so thick that in time ice formed, producing thousands of alpine glaciers. These remain in part to this day at some places within the United States and at many more localities in Canada. Those in Glacier National Park, although but the shrunken remnants of glaciers that were once many miles in length, are visited by thousands of tourists annually. Though they exhibit many of the characteristics of high-mountain glaciers, they are tiny in comparison to their ancestors.

The glaciers in the Rocky Mountains of Canada are far more spectacular than those remaining in the United States. Tongues of ice ranging up to fifteen miles in length are frequent along the route from Banff to Jasper. The high-mountain areas of the Canadian Rockies contain considerable remnants of ice sheets. The Columbia Icefield and the Clemenceau Icecap, both of which are in part within the area of Jasper National Park, may be visited without much difficulty. The Athabaska Glacier has its source in the Columbia Icefield and extends at least ten miles to the eastward through a mountain canyon.

A visit to the lower end of the Athabaska Glacier is a grand experience. The ice, which is constantly moving forward, is melting continuously, and streams of cold water issue from beneath the glacier. When the streams leave the great mass of ice, the warm air causes more melting, so that large caves are formed, roofed over with the clear, turquoise-colored ice. In the roofs of the caves great cracks develop, and blocks of ice fall into the streams. Waters trickling into the caves from the surface of the glacier freeze, edging them with fringes of long icicles, creating a realm of breath-taking beauty, a fairyland of colors and delicate forms. Fortunately, it is possible to record some of these scenes on color films.

In front of this, the most accessible of the Canadian glaciers, there is an area, at least equal to a square mile in extent, mantled with sand, gravels, clay, and boulders left by the ice as the glacier front retreated. This glacial debris is very roughly distributed. Here are hills and ridges of various sizes, and without any order or arrangement. Between the high places there are basins or hollows, some of which contain ponds or lakes. The entire area is as yet without vegetation. It is an empty, desolate-looking place, dull-gray in color. A few years more must pass before a true soil is formed and seeds get started. If you have ever had difficulty in picturing how much of the

United States looked as the great ice sheets disappeared, an hour or two at and about the lower end of the Athabaska Glacier will show you the gray, barren landscape of an earlier age.

South of Glacier National Park, there is little left of the ice that thousands of years ago covered the mountains. Only a few perennial snow fields endure. These are "dead" glaciers, little ice fields that have lost their force. And yet the geologist easily discovers the evidences of grinding and gouging by the ice in the high mountain valleys. More than that, he finds deposits made by the glaciers far down the valleys, and even out on the plains. Even in the San Juans, the most southern mountain group of the Rockies, there are deposits which show that the glaciers were commonly twenty miles in length. One tongue of ice was fifty miles long.

One of the most significant deposits made by ice lies at the west base of the Wasatch Mountains. Here huge, long mounds of mixed sand, clay, and boulders, called moraines, lie on the slopes of a lake that existed during glacial times. This lake, known as Lake Bonneville, was immense. Its remnant today is Great Salt Lake. These deposits consist of materials which the mountain glaciers eroded from the high valleys. The great force of the ice is attested to by the size of the boulders. In the Wind River Range, boulders ten feet in diameter are scattered over the land. Many times the irregularly deposited moraines act as dams, and they account for many of the mountain lakes that now reflect the blue of the mountain skies.

Two of the most dramatically glaciated areas are Glacier National Park and Yellowstone National Park. The gouged-out amphitheaters of the valley heads (or cirques) in Glacier

National Park hold little cirque lakes that mirror the peaks in their still waters. The great U-shaped gorges in the middle reaches of the valleys testify to the tremendous force of the ice. The valleys are frequently bare of soil, so recently has the gouging-out taken place. Every visitor to the Yellowstone has had pointed out to him the monumental boulder on the west side of the canyon as evidence of what carrying power a glacier has. From the character of the rock we know that this boulder was brought from the Absaroka Range to the east. Obviously, it was brought to its position before the Yellowstone Canyon was excavated. This means that the canyon, 1,200 feet deep, was cut since the glacial period, a matter of 25,000 to 30,000 years ago.*

Why are the valley glaciers shrinking and, indeed, disappearing? Climate fluctuates as if controlled by some cosmic pendulum. There has been a score of glacial periods in the geologic past, chilling intervals in an otherwise torrid world. The end of the Great Ice Age of which we are speaking was marked by a great reduction in the amount of snowfall, so that the perennial fields of snow and ice became less and less in thickness and extent. As the climate grew warmer, melting was in excess of accumulation. Little by little these alpine tongues of ice became shorter. They did not move backward; they were continually moving forward, as all glaciers do as long as they exist, but they were melting so rapidly that each season they became shorter. This is beautifully illustrated to-day by many of the glaciers in the Canadian Rockies. Heaps of morainic debris in front of these glaciers are without any

* Geologically speaking, a short time.

sign of vegetation, and appear to have been left but yesterday by ice. Throughout the areas of modern glaciers where rapid melting is taking place, milky-white streams of icy waters are carrying away the finer material, or rock flour, formed beneath these huge, moving masses of ice.

The great continental ice sheets which formed during this last Great Ice Age in North America have all disappeared. There is nothing left at any one of the centers in the northeastern part of the continent, and only bits of former ice sheets remain in the cordilleran area. The icecap of Greenland and those on some of the small islands in the Arctic Archipelago are but shrunken remnants of greater ice sheets. Even in Alaska there are no true icecaps, but there are mountain glaciers in all of the higher mountain regions of that territory.

When the alpine glaciers of the Rocky Mountains finally melted away, the canyons which they occupied showed many indications of the former presence of the ice. Stream-cut gorges in the mountains are V-shaped in form. Those through which glaciers have moved are U-shaped. That is one of the most fundamental of the changes which take place in mountain regions that are glaciated. When a glacier moves through a canyon, it deepens, as well as widens, the gorge, and, if the tributary valleys are not equally deepened, these valleys, after the ice disappears, end high on the main canyon walls. They are hanging valleys, and from them streams plunge in foaming cascades to the valley floor.

At the head of the valley is the catchment basin. Farther downstream, the glacier did less wearing away and more depositing. The morainic deposits dammed the valleys and created elongated lakes. Moraines lie across the valley. So-called lateral moraines lie on the valley walls, parallel to the stream course. The valley is chaotic with morainic hills and ridges, a great confusion. The scars of glacial wearing away and depositing have been too recently formed to be healed.

Toward the head of each glaciated canyon there are likely to be a number of steps, where the ancient glacier was at work, lowering the floor of the canyon, and at the head of each glaciated gorge there is a large amphitheatral area, the cirque. It was in the cirques that the snows accumulated and were compressed into the ice which formed the last glacier. Not until a considerable amount of ice rested in a catchment basin was there any movement. As that movement proceeded, it was necessarily down valley, away from the great rock walls of the catchment basin.

The large amphitheatral cirques in the high mountain regions are among the most striking of scenic features. Their bounding walls are nearly vertical, and the floors of many of them are not very uneven. As the ice moved away from the high bounding walls, carrying rock material with it, the walls were slightly undermined. This caused slumping, and the consequent retreat of the vertical wall. In this way the cirques became larger and larger. At many places on the floors of the cirques there are morainic masses of debris, which form lake basins, and some spots, where the ice has gouged basins out of the solid rock. These rock basins are almost certain to contain lakes. The tiny remnants of the alpine glaciers that remain to this day are in the basin regions. They rest on the floors of cirques where the ice formed.

191

There were at least three distinct stages of glaciation, perhaps more. Each stage, or period, of glaciation covers the forming of the ice, the advance of that ice through the canyon, the melting and final disappearance of the ice. There follows an interglacial stage when the climate is mild. The opening of another period requires a change in climate and a repetition of the sequence of events that gave character to the earlier period of ice action.

We have come to look upon the Great Ice Age in North America as one in which a series of climatic changes occurred. During each very cold period there were heavy snowfalls, which caused the formation of the ice. Each warm period, with less snowfall, caused the disappearance of the ice. We may look upon the present as a period when the ice is waning or disappearing. We are living under climatic conditions such as must have existed in the closing stages of earlier periods of ice. Since there are glaciers in portions of the Rocky Mountains and in far northern parts of the continent, we are not really through with the Ice Age today.

During the summer of 1944, my last field season with a pack train in the Rocky Mountains before completing all work on the manuscript for this volume, I discovered a most remarkable glacial deposit on the very crestline or summit of the Gravelly Range of southwestern Montana. The range had received its name, "Gravelly," because of loose, waterworn deposits on the summit in which prospectors have found gold. The possibility of having discovered the source of the remarkable Alder Creek deposits, near Virginia City, where some

192

sixty million dollars worth of gold has been recovered, has long attracted attention to this range of mountains.

True, there is gold in some portions of this deposit on the summit of the range, but there are striated stones and boulders and every other indication necessary to prove that the deposit which gives the range its name is of glacial origin. The strange thing about it is that a glacial moraine, which was deposited in the bottom of a mountain valley, is now at the crestline of a mountain range.

These conditions require some imagination. When the moraine was deposited, there were high mountains on either side, and in those mountains alpine glaciers formed. Those glaciers descended into the valleys and there left the sands, gravels, and boulders. The waters associated with those glaciers brought with them fragments of gold-bearing ore. That gold has remained for millions of years in that glacial moraine. Those mountains from which the ice descended have all disappeared. They may have risen five or six thousand feet above the present crestline, but they are all gone and there is nothing but blue sky where they once stood. Then, when the mountain mass rose again, streams dissected still further the rock of the mountains, and the moraine which was in the low place has preserved the rock immediately beneath it and come to be the high place, the crestline, the summit of the range.

This discovery has more than passing interest to those who would know the story of the mountains, for the ice which left this moraine formed some sixty million years ago, long before the great Ice Age which deposited the moraines commonly observed in the mountains of today. This is a very ancient glacial moraine which has been preserved through the ages. As rain waters fall in this area, they sink in and pass through this gravelly material; they do not wash it away. The moraine has thus served as a preserving cap and now comes to be the crestline of a mountain.

Most of the glaciers on the earth are melting away, and our climate may, as the centuries pass, become still milder; the summers may be a little longer, the fall of snow a little less, and subtropical conditions may advance farther and farther from the equator. There is evidence that in certain of the earlier interglacial periods on this continent the climate became much milder than it has been since the last melting away of alpine glaciers in the Rocky Mountains of our country. It is not impossible that the present period of deglaciation will be followed by another period when ice will form again in the empty cirques of the lofty mountains and on the far northern lands of this continent.

CHAPTER ELEVEN

BONANZA IN THE ROCKIES

Where roots of trees pry rocks apart. The tree is searching for moisture. As the root grows, it has a tremendous prying force and lifts great masses of rock or splits apart the fragments it has made. The field worker is measuring the direction of glacial markings on the rock surface.

Upturned strata in the foothill belt of the Rockies, in Montana.

Panning for gold.

A ghost town in the San Juan Mountains of Colorado.

With what excitement did the Spanish explorers first view the great peaks of the Rockies! Coming from the south, they discovered the mountains in New Mexico and Colorado. From there they went westward and southwestward over what was called the Spanish Trail to southern California. There are stories, among the old-timers in the mountains, of rich ore deposits located by these early explorers and never relocated. They are the basis of many a "lost-cabin-mine."

The legend invariably runs this way. An early Spanish explorer locates a rich ore deposit, builds a cabin, takes out all the gold he can carry, makes a map to show the location of his claim, and leaves for home. He is immensely wealthy, and after he dies, a map is found among his papers giving the location of a mine in America. Expeditions are organized to locate the cabin and the mine. The first party comes from Spain with the original map. They work for months but give up the hunt. Just before leaving for home, they sell or give the map to some American prospector. This leads to the organization of other searching parties. Year after year people come in to look for the "lost-cabin-mine." I remember being told of one of the early Spanish prospectors who built a cabin, mined all the gold he could carry, and, in leaving for the outside, had to reshoe his saddle horse. Having nothing else, he made nails of gold that held the shoes on the horse's feet until he reached a settlement. He himself tried over and over again in vain to find his old cabin. No one has found it yet.

It was the fur trade in North America that early led many adventurous trappers into the more northerly portions of the Rocky Mountains. Some of them later became miners. When Lewis and Clark went on their long exploring expedition to the Northwest in 1804-06; they met a few white people in the Montana portion of the Rocky Mountains.

But in 1848, when gold was discovered in the stream gravels of California, a great westward movement was inaugurated. Vast numbers of people, following various trails, traveled over the Great Plains, through the mountain area, across the semidesert Great Basin region, and finally over the Sierra Nevada. During this stampede to the West, the Oregon Trail was traversed by thousands. That weary road followed the valley of the Sweetwater River in Wyoming and crossed the Bear River Range into the broad plateau lands of the Snake River country. After crossing the Rocky Mountains, the gold seekers struck off by a trail to the southwest for California; those heading for Oregon went northwestward to the valley of the Columbia, and then westward.

The vision of gold in California led most of the adventurers to hurry through the Rocky Mountain region and press on to the Pacific coastal area. Some of the men, while on their way, camped in river valleys among the Rockies where the gravel "looked promising." At each stopping place someone would take out a few pans of sand and gravel, wash the material, and test it for its gold content. Few finds of importance were made in those early days but there was sufficient yellow in the sands in the Rocky Mountain stream courses to remind men who failed to make great fortunes in California of the possibilities farther to the east. Later, many of the treasure hunters returned to the region of the Rocky Mountains, and others coming westward chose to begin their prospecting in this area.

THE COMING OF THE AMERICAN PROSPECTORS

By 1860 there were hundreds of men looking about in the Rocky Mountains for "pay streaks" in the stream gravels, or scrambling over the hills searching for "float" rock, which appeared to carry precious minerals that would guide them to rich mineral veins. These prospectors were the vanguard of the thousands who came later to seek out the mineral wealth of the mountains.

The typical prospector is a most interesting American personality. He is endowed with unlimited hope and courage. Day in and day out, after sampling stream gravels or hunting on the mountainside for specimens which he thinks may be pay dirt, he returns to his lonely camp, where he may have nothing but a five-dollar burro as a companion. After cooking and eating his simple meal, he sits down by a little campfire, lights his pipe, and dreams of the fortune that is "just around the

199

hill." In the next hole he sinks he surely will find a pay streak. Then he will sink a much larger hole, follow the pay streak, take out hundreds, thousands, and possibly millions of dollars' worth of gold. If he finds small grains of gold in his first pan, he will work upstream toward the source of the yellow metal, finding coarser and coarser grains, and possibly nuggets worth a thousand dollars each. He will soon have piles of yellow gold too great to carry. His dream becomes a vision. Now a rich man, he will return home. The sun sets. He crawls into his lonely camp bed, drops off to sleep, only to continue his dream.

The next morning he prepares a few slices of bacon, a mountain trout hooked in a near-by stream, a cup of coffee, and some baking-powder biscuits, which he cooks in a Dutch oven. Two or three left-over strips of bacon, sandwiched into cold, lumpy biscuits, go into his pack for lunch, and he is off for another day, with pick and shovel over one shoulder and gold pan under his arm.

The little burro that serves as pack animal on moving days is assistant to his master, and companion as well. He carries a bed, tent, the dishes, and camp utensils, and possibly the pick and shovel. His keep costs nothing, for he earns his own living afterhours, on moving days, and while the boss is off prospecting, by nibbling the grasses, shrubs, wild flowers, thistles, and the wrappers on tin cans. Since he may be feeling independent when he is left in camp all day, he is put on the end of a long, firmly anchored rope. There is a little danger of his hanging himself, but his boss prefers to take that risk rather than allow him to wreck the camp.

200

PLACER MINING

The working of placer deposits is one of the simplest and least expensive methods of mining. The washing of gravels can be done with very little equipment. A one-man sluice box, eight or ten feet long, and a pick and shovel will answer the purpose. A small group of workmen can form a company, set up a series of sluice boxes, and so divide the work of shoveling, directing the flow of water, and clearing away the tailings. Several tons of gravel are washed each day. A little grating is placed in the bottom of each unit box. As the water, carrying the sand and gravel, flows over these crosspieces, or cleats, there is a constant churning, caused by the rippling motion of the water, and the heavier particles naturally become lodged or caught behind the cleats.

After washing has continued for several days, the water is turned off, and the men have a "clean-up day." They lift the gratings, brush them carefully, and remove them from the sluice boxes. If gold is on the bottom of the sluice box, it is then scraped together and taken to the assay office. At the end of most sluice boxes, several feet are coated with mercury, so that the very finest dust, or flour, of gold will be caught and amalgamated. When the amalgam is scraped off, it must be taken to a laboratory and heated to vaporize the mercury. Thus, the gold in the amalgam is recovered.

A prospector concentrating on placer deposits selects for sampling one place after another in the stream gravels of some valley. Since gold is the heaviest mineral found in stream

201

courses, and is much heavier than the rock materials, it settles
through the gravel and sand deposits toward the bedrock.
Gold is nearly twice as heavy as lead, more than twice as heavy
as iron, and a little more than seven times as heavy as quartz.
There is not very much chance of getting "a good pan of dirt"
from the surface gravels in a stream course. Therefore, it is
necessary to go some little distance from the immediate stream
and sink a hole in the gravel of some portion of the flood plain
not now covered by water. It may be necessary to dig two or
three feet, or as much as eight or ten feet, in order to reach
bedrock. Those who located the rich placer deposits near Virginia City in Montana went from ten to fifteen feet through
coarse gravel. The pay-streak where the grains, or flakes, of
gold are concentrated is likely to be within a few inches of
the solid bedrock of the stream channel. About two shovelfuls
of the sand and gravel believed to contain gold are taken
as a sample, placed in a pan, and washed.

A well-made gold pan is circular and about eighteen inches
in diameter. It has a flat bottom and sloping sides about four
inches in width. In carrying out the panning process, the prospector goes to the margin of a stream and fills the pan to the
brim with water. At first he mixes the sand and gravel as
thoroughly as possible without allowing it to overflow. He
holds the pan horizontally for a time, shakes the material,
using a rotary motion all the time. When the mixing has been
accomplished, the pan is tipped a little so that some of the
water and the lighter grains of sand and silt may overflow.
The rotary motion continues, with the pan tilted slightly. He

is working on the principle that the heavier material will go to the bottom of the pan. With each rotation, he allows a little more of the lighter sand and gravel to overflow with some of the water. If he loses much of the water in this process, he puts more into the pan and continues shaking the material more or less as he rotates it, in order to free the tiny grains of gold so that they can sink to the bottom of the pan. He works all the time with the expectation that when he comes near the close of the washing process he will see in the crease at the margin of the flat base of the pan a little area of bright-yellow grains. A single pan of dirt has been known to yield as much as five hundred dollars' worth of gold, but a pan that yields twenty cents' worth is often a clue to a deposit that is worth working. The whole process may take ten or fifteen minutes. This obtaining of gold from loose gravels is known as placer mining.

Once a pay streak has been located, the prospector plans at once to stake off one, two, or three claims along the stream bed where he thinks the gold is located. In the early days each claim was one hundred feet in length and extended from bank to bank. He then puts in corner posts. In a tin can near one of the posts, he places his name and an account of his having staked off the claim. Claims should be recorded at the nearest county seat as soon as possible. In order to hold a mining claim, a man is required to do at least one hundred dollars' worth of work on it, in the development of the property, each year. That is known as assessment work.

A great many difficulties have arisen because men have

neglected a claim and someone else has come in and begun to work it—a procedure known as "jumping a claim." It may mean a fist fight or a shooting, or it may mean a lawsuit.

Men have been known to stake off a claim, sink a hole to bedrock, add gold dust to the gravel at the bottom of the hole dug for sampling, and then offer the property for sale. Prospective purchasers are invited to take their samples from the bottom of the pit with their own hands and have them carefully assayed. Of course, the results are A-1, and the sale is quickly consummated. Of course, too, the original staker promptly disappears. It is not healthy to stay on the scene after a performance known as "salting a mine."

There are plenty of opportunities for fraud in the mining business, but even if there were no treachery or deceit it is a game in which there is a large element of risk. A mining man must be willing to take a chance. In many of the most remarkable cases, it is the men with courage and a willingness to gamble who have made the huge fortunes which have come from this mountain area.

The ore of tin, called cassiterite, is so heavy that it tends to accumulate in the bottom of stream gravels and can be reclaimed by placer mining. Tin ores are very scarce in North America, though sufficient amounts have been found in the stream gravels of the Black Hills to encourage many mining ventures. This tin ore is jet black and can be recognized both by its color and its weight. It is the same kind of tin ore that is mined in large quantities in the Malay Peninsula. We need tin greatly, and it is not impossible that some day we may discover a rich deposit of tin somewhere in North America. Alaska has produced a small amount but nowhere in the Rocky Mountains, except in the Black Hills, has tin mining amounted to very much.

Long before all the worth-while gravel in the stream bed has been washed and the gold or tin reclaimed, some of the mining men in that vicinity will start hunting for the original source of the mineral wealth. They know it came down the hills into the stream courses, and they reason correctly that there must be mineral veins that reach the surface somewhere in the drainage basin above, or upstream, from the placer deposits. Therefore, someone by hunting should locate some of those mineral veins. A mineral vein that is worth mining is called an ore, and the body of ore being worked in solid rock is referred to as a lode. Thus, lode mining commonly follows the development of placer mining in any great mineralized area.

The prospector searching for mineral veins examines all rock outcrops that attract his eye, and as he works higher and higher on the mountain he heads for the bare rock surfaces that look good to him. He is usually attracted by highly colored rock materials. Every quartz vein must be examined with special care. Quartz is one of the commonest of the minerals filling the cracks or fissures in the rocks, and, while it is being precipitated, free or metallic gold also may be deposited. Prospectors are guided somewhat by the weight, color, hardness, and luster of the rock specimens. Certain minerals, such as lead and zinc, are very heavy, and the commonest ore of lead looks like a metal. Certain ores of copper are bright green and others are azure blue. One of the very rich ores of copper, chalcocite, is very dark blue, almost black. That is the ore which has made Butte one of the richest mining centers in the world.

If anyone has even an elementary knowledge of minerals, he may, by simple tests which he can make in the field, identify most of the minerals he is likely to find, and many of the prospectors become very good practical men in the identification of minerals. Since the mineral wealth in a rock specimen is very often not visible to the naked eye, the prospector must take the specimens he thinks valuable to an assay office to have them examined by laboratory methods, and to have the quantity of precious metals accurately weighed.

In sampling a vein, one should clear off all loose surface material and take a fair sample of all the materials from one wall of the vein to the other. He should make an honest cross-section cut, taking an equal amount from each fraction of the vein. The rock material thus taken must next be pulverized. Then it should be placed on a flat surface in the form of a low dome or circular mound. Now it is ready for the first quartering. The mound is divided into four equal parts, much as a pie might be cut into four equal pieces. The alternate quarters are then taken, and the others are discarded or laid aside for another sampling. If the first and third quarters are taken the first time, the second and fourth are taken after the next quartering. Each time the part taken or held is thoroughly mixed, heaped up, and made into a dome half the size of the preceding dome. This process of quartering and retaining one half is carried on until the amount left is a reasonable sample for carrying to the assay office. It will usually be about one pound of ore.

If the report from the assay office is encouraging, samples at other places across the vein should be taken. At intervals holes should be sunk deep enough to determine whether the ore continues into the earth. The vein should be followed on the surface, and the angle at which it dips into the earth should be recorded. A sketch map showing the location of the claim and the outcrops of rock formations adjoining the mineral vein should be made. Careful preliminary studies and honest sampling may avoid many a disappointment. In some portions of the Rocky Mountains, the hillsides have been dug into at hundreds of places, and below each hole there is a little pile of rock waste. The picture suggests the work of gophers that have been digging their homes on the side of a mountain. I had a ranchman packer with me one season who, when he saw such a hillside, said: "If I owned those mines I would cut them up for postholes." There are many disappointments in the life of a prospector.

After sampling and assaying have been done, and the conviction is justified that a worth-while body of ore has been located, men frequently form small partnerships and go to work to sink a shaft into the body of ore. Others form a company and, after working out the dip of the ore body, plan to drive a tunnel into the side of the mountain several hundred feet below the outcrop of the ore body. In this way they expect to intersect the ore body deep in the mountain and, by overhead work, break the ore into fragments which can be dropped into an ore car, rolled out, and dumped into a crushing mill. This method is much more satisfactory than sinking from the surface on an ore body.

In the development of large mining properties, the services of expert mining geologists are engaged, so that the rock structure can be worked out in detail. The location of the veins must be projected into the earth with a high degree of accuracy. If faults or breaks have occurred in the structure, they must be measured and taken into account. If different mineral veins have been located, each one should, if possible, be identified and kept distinct in the plotting of the ore bodies. No large bodies of ore in these mountains have been developed without sinking shafts hundreds of feet into the ground and driving tunnels at different levels. The tunnels are so driven that the ore bodies can be intersected at various levels.

In the development of large properties in which hundreds of men are at work underground, plans are made for forcing fresh air into the shafts and tunnels. The mines are virtually air-conditioned artificially. Provision must be made underground for the sharpening of drills and for the repair of machinery. When mules or horses are used in drawing the ore cars, stables for the animals are built deep in the earth. Most of the mines are now lighted with electricity, and some of them have trolley cars for hauling ore and for the workers to use in traveling to and from the shaft, where they are lowered to the level on which they are working. Restrooms, hospitals, offices, and lunchrooms are provided. There are little underground cities in some of the very large mines of this mountain area.

208

The young men in the office, working under the direction of expert mining engineers, keep records of each ore body as it is sampled from day to day; they work out the value of each block of ore and can estimate the value of the output from the mine for each day. They prepare maps of all underground workings and keep them up to date. At times the office force prepares models of the mines, showing all shafts, tunnels, ore bodies, and the geologic structures at each level, some of them so constructed that they can be taken apart to show just what conditions obtain at different levels. These models are sometimes used in court when lawsuits are being argued, in order to explain the conditions underground to a judge or to a jury.

The practical mining men who go underground are continually on the lookout for new bodies of ore. Whenever a tunnel is being driven, they examine every foot of rock wall as the blasting advances. They are watching for new mineral veins, faults, or any changes in structure that might guide them in developing the property.

MONTANA MINE YARNS

François Finlay is credited with having made the first discovery of gold in Montana. He was one of the men who had learned how to wash the gold from stream gravels in California. On his return to Montana in 1852, he found "colors" on the western slopes of the Rocky Mountains in a little tributary to Hell Gate River called Gold Creek. Various other reports of gold in Montana stream gravels came in during the succeeding years. In 1862 a pay streak was found in a small tributary on the eastern slope of the Bitterroot Mountains, and in the following year the town of Bannack was established, in order to accommodate the miners working in that vicinity. It is reported that the placer deposits near Bannack yielded about $4,000,000.

One of the most spectacular of all the discoveries made in Montana was located on the valley floor of Alder Creek. To-day that valley floor, for eight or ten miles below Virginia City, is a continuous belt, 100 to 1,500 feet in width, of small conical hills of gravel. It is one of the roughest, most hummocky bits of topography to be found anywhere. The entire bottom land of the stream course has been worked over by steamshovels or by hand, so that every pay streak that might possibly be located in that valley could be dug up and put through a series of sluice boxes in order to recover the gold that was present. By 1868, $30,000,000 had been taken from the gravels of this one valley, and the thriving, bustling, pioneer mining town, Virginia City, had been established.

The story of Alder Creek starts with William Fairweather, a prospector who, in the spring of 1863, when returning from Yellowstone, worn and tired and disheartened, camped by a little stream near the north end of Gravelly Range. From habit he sampled the gravel in that stream for gold. From his first pan he recovered $1.75 worth. Other places yielded good results, and Fairweather, with four other members of his party, immediately staked off claims. They had located what proved to be the richest placer diggings in Montana. Near the head of the ravine, which is about nine miles south of Virginia

City, the gravels carried nuggets, each worth hundreds of dollars. The largest nugget yet found there was valued at $800. Downstream, most of the gold was in small, bright-yellow grains and, as the stream was constantly dropping the heavier particles in its load, the gold in the pay streak far down the valley became as fine as dust, or delicate flakes, and some was even spoken of as "flour gold."

By 1865, Virginia City, with a population of 10,000 became the capital of the territory of Montana. To this honor, Virginia City succeeded Bannack, another center of placer mining, which was the first capital of the territory. At about this same time, gold was recovered from the gravel in streams near the site of Helena, and in 1874 that city, which had become a thriving and promising mining center, became the capital of the territory. Montana became a state in 1889, with Helena as its permanent capital. The people of that state have been partial to their mining centers.

Today the old placer diggings near Helena are just heaps of gravel, where little or no work is carried on. Occasionally a single miner may be seen grubbing through the tailings of earlier days in order to make a living. There is a story told in Helena that in 1884, when a foundation was to be dug for the Montana National Bank, the contractor agreed to accept the excavated gravel as payment for his work. That was because Main Street in Helena is an old stream bed, and the unworked portion was believed to contain rich deposits of placer gold.

THE BUTTE REGION

The Butte region of Montana was first a placer-gold territory, with mining activities centered in the early sixties at Silver Bow Creek, at the base of the hill on which Butte is located. The discovery was made in 1864 by a group of miners from Alder Creek, who staked off claims far up the hills, where the great mines of today are located. Hundreds flocked after them, to try their luck in the district, and two years later the town of Butte was established.

Each of the stream beds carried some gold, and this naturally led to prospecting for mineral veins all over the hillside. The first lode was located in 1864, but the ore did not contain enough free milling gold to be satisfactory. The ores at Butte contain cold, silver, lead, zinc, and copper. They are complex, and the treatment of such ores presented difficult problems. For some time the camp languished. The outlook was so gloomy that many of the mining men left town, discouraged.

In 1875 William Farlin built a stamp mill and introduced a new process in the treatment of the ores. He had assay reports that showed wealth in silver and copper, and he had learned how to extract such values. By 1876 when Farlin was doing fairly well, one of the great characters in western mining history, William A. Clark, later Senator Clark, appeared on the scene. Clark was a dynamic character and a very successful promoter. His notable energy and ability in the organization of mining enterprises and in the treatment of the ores soon produced big returns. In 1878 the output at Butte was valued

212

at $1,174,000. By a curious coincidence, another famous personality in the American mining industry, Marcus Daly, arrived at Butte in 1876. To Clark and Daly should go the credit for making the mining of copper at Butte a great success. They built stamp mills for crushing the ores, furnaces for roasting ores, and, by 1880, the first smelter.

In 1882, George Hearst, who later became United States Senator, and whose son was the newspaper publisher, came to Butte. He directed the sinking of a shaft which led, at a depth of 300 feet, to the discovery of a very rich copper lode, five feet thick. That discovery and the building of smelters for reducing the ores boosted copper mining in Butte. About this same time railroad connections were established with the Union Pacific line at Ogden, and in 1893 the Northern Pacific road reached Butte. These were days of rapid development in the Rocky Mountain region. Huge fortunes were being made and the population was increasing rapidly.

In 1887 the production of silver in Butte reached its peak. There were 290 stamps working, treating 400 tons of ore daily, with a yield of $25.00 per ton, a total of $10,000 in values per day. There followed a series of exciting years. For a time, Clark and Daly, two very strong personalities and the most prominent citizens of Butte, were cordial friends. Later they became rivals, and in the end bitter enemies. Clark bought more and more mines, built huge reduction plants for treating ores, became very wealthy, and emerged as the outstanding political figure in the district. Daly built a new and very large smelter at Anaconda and spent half a million dollars trying to make that city the capital of Montana. Clark opposed this plan and succeeded in making Helena the capital. Daly and Clark each purchased newspapers to help them in their fight, and some unkind words were published. For ten years Daly prevented Clark's election to the United States Senate. When, in 1899, Clark was finally elected Daly waged a fight in Washington which cost him $25,000 and forced Clark to resign his seat. Both men were Democrats, but they fought bitterly, and each had a fortune with which to work.

In hills like the one at Butte, Montana, where the rock is richly mineralized, there is keen competition among the mining men. Many ore bodies are discovered, shafts are sunk at various locations, and thousands of feet of tunneling are completed. In 1940 there were fifty-eight actively producing mines in this one district. The underground workings reached a depth of 1,200 feet in several of the mines, and of more than 4,000 feet in some. The interlacing tunnels from the many shafts make a complicated network of passageways about 2,700 miles long. In this underground realm, the men working in different mines have sometimes come together, one group following a vein from one direction and one from the other. Such a meeting is distinctly dramatic. Each group accuses the other of stealing their ore. A great iron door may be put in the tunnel where the miners met. Claims are filed, lawsuits are brought, and in due time each side comes into court with maps, models, diagrams, and with mining engineers, geologists, and keen lawyers to help them prove that the other fellows are in the wrong and have no right to the ore they are mining. Each party holds that the other must return a large sum of money for the ore they have already taken from the vein in question.

The trials may drag on for months, or years, with the scientific and technical witnesses receiving at least a hundred dollars a day when retained, and the lawyers reaping fortunes.

The story of the Butte mining district is crowded with dramatic incidents, and it is a record of wonderful discoveries which have led to the development of fabulous wealth. The hill at Butte is certainly one of the most richly mineralized areas in the world. The payroll during the Second World War boom of 1943 is reported at $4,000,000 per month.

"PIKES PEAK OR BUST"

Colorado, too, contributes its share of mining yarns. In the stampede of "forty-niners," who were rushing to California to have a share in the gold that had been reported in the stream gravels of that part of the country, was a group of Cherokee Indians from Georgia. These Indians knew something of gold mining before they started, and as they crossed through Colorado, they tested some of the gravels in the stream courses near Pikes Peak and found just enough gold to hold their attention and to lead them to report their discoveries. Others followed them, and in 1858 a party of nine men, organized in Georgia, came to the Pikes Peak region in the hope of locating rich placer deposits. They were fairly well rewarded. The story of the gold in the creeks around Pikes Peak spread like wildfire. Thousands of people started from Missouri, Kansas, and adjoining areas, traveling overland in covered wagons, on horseback, or in oxcarts to the newly discovered gold-fields, flaunting their slogan, glaringly painted on wagons, carts, and

215

saddles: "Pikes Peak or Bust." By fall, many of them were homeward bound, in battered vehicles labeled with the one word, "Busted."

The 1859 stampede to Pikes Peak is one of the few historic gold rushes in the history of our western country that proved a failure. It attracted so much attention that Horace Greeley, then Editor of the *New York Tribune*, joined a group of other newspapermen and visited the gold-fields of Colorado in order to report to his paper eye-witness accounts of the mining activities and development of the West that had roused such popular interest and excitement. The following statement, as quoted by Percy S. Fritz in "Colorado, the Centennial State," was published by Horace Greeley in about 1859:

"Gold mining is a business which eminently requires of its votaries, capital, experience, energy, and endurance, and in which the highest qualities do not always command success. . . . There are said to be five thousand people already in this ravine (Gregory Gulch), and hundreds pouring into it daily. Tens of thousands more have been passed by us on our rapid journey to this place, or heard of as on their way hither by other routes. For all these, nearly every pound of provisions and supplies of every kind must be hauled by teams from the Missouri River some seven hundred miles distant, over roads which are mere trails, crossing countless unbridged watercourses, always steep-banked, and often mirey, and at times so swollen by rains as to be utterly impassable by wagons. Part of this distance is a desert, yielding grass, wood and water only at intervals of several miles, and then very scantily. To at-

216

tempt to cross this desert on foot is madness—suicide—murder. To cross it with teams in midsummer, when the watercourses are mainly dry, and the grass eaten up, is possible only to those who know just where to look for grass and water, and where water must be carried along to preserve life.

"A few months hence, [sic]—probably by the middle of October, [sic]—this whole Alpine region will be snowed under and frozen up so as to put a stop to the working of sluices if not to mining altogether. There then, for a period of at least six months, will be neither employment, food, nor shelter within five hundred miles for the thousands pressing hither under the delusion that gold may be picked up here like pebbles on the seashore, and that when they arrive here, even though without provisions or money, their fortunes are made. Great disappointment, great suffering, are inevitable; few can escape the latter who arrive at Denver City after September without ample means to suppor[t] them in a very dear country, at least through a long winter. We charge those who manage the telegraph not to diffuse a part of our statement without giving substantially the whole. . . ."

Since no really great discoveries were made during the first stampede to the Pikes Peak region, most of the miners drifted away into other portions of the mountain area. However, that mighty mountain, which stands 14,107 feet above sea level, 4,000 to 5,000 feet conspicuously above the general level of the Rocky Mountains, kept attracting prospectors.

George M. Pullman was one of the adventurers drawn to Colorado by the reports of gold. After his invention of the

American type of sleeping car, he said that he had obtained his first idea of such a car from the double-deck bunks used in the mining camps. Mr. Pullman held several claims in the Pikes Peak region and, in 1864 he sold a number of them at $1,000 per linear foot. In those days each claim was a hundred feet long, and it is reported that this sale gave Mr. Pullman his start on the road to success and wealth. After disposing of his mines in the Pikes Peak region, he went to Central City, Colorado, another mining center, where he ran a hardware store for a number of years.

CRIPPLE CREEK

On the southwest slope of Pikes Peak, near Cripple Creek, there is a very striking knob called Mt. Pisgah where, several years after the "Pikes Peak stampede," new finds of gold were reported. Miners assembled in the vicinity of this hill in 1884. Many of them had been unable to find gold in workable quantities in the various prospecting holes which they had sunk. Some thought that they had been deceived, and that the claims they had purchased had been "salted." They were a disappointed group, and they left the place in a state of utter discouragement and disgust. For the second time, widespread interest had been aroused by their venture, and its collapse did not help the reputation of the Pikes Peak region. Colorado people refer to it, even now, as "the Mt. Pisgah fiasco."

There was one man, Robert Womack, who refused to be discouraged and remained. He did not have sufficient funds to devote himself to prospecting. Therefore, he worked on a small ranch in the district, prospecting during his free time. He was really a cowboy, and his companions in the saddle laughed, good-naturedly, at his persistence in prospecting round the south slopes of Pikes Peak. In 1890 he was rewarded by the discovery of a very promising, small but rich, vein in Poverty Gulch, where he had sunk a shaft forty-eight feet deep. He sold his option on the claim for $5,000.

The discoveries that really put Cripple Creek on the mining map were made by W. S. Stratton. He was a carpenter by trade, who had the habit of prospecting when he was not engaged in his regular work. He had learned how to use a blowpipe and had sufficient knowledge to detect valuable minerals that many of the prospectors ignored. Stratton moved into the region where Womack was located. There he was shown a specimen that looked like the common ore of lead, galena, but Stratton said he didn't think it was the common lead ore. He went to work with his blowpipe and from that specimen he obtained a "button of gold." He had found an ore called a telluride, rarely known to miners in those days, but it was this ore that made the Cripple Creek region famous among the mining districts of Colorado and one of the best-known mining centers in the world.

The first miner who ever discovered a telluride of gold is said to have noticed it at a campfire, in which chunks of rock, set to hold the cooking pots, had become overheated and begun to sweat gold. Actually, the ore had been roasted, and the telluride had released little globules of gold. An accident such as that is not impossible.

The Cripple Creek discoveries of the early nineties proved

that lode mining must be done on a large scale. Considerable capital had to be employed before any returns could be expected. Expensive equipment and all mining supplies were brought on muleback high into the mountains. At the mining camp, repair shops, assay laboratories, offices, stores, and homes had to be provided. Shafts were sunk and tunnels driven. Mills were erected where the ores could be treated, so that not the ores but the concentrates were taken to the smelters in Pueblo or Denver.

With the establishment of smelters in Colorado, Meyer Guggenheim, whose seven sons have played such an important part in the ore-refining industry and in public life in this country, comes into the annals of this mining region. Meyer Guggenheim came to Colorado in the boom days of mining. He took some interest in the mines, but decided to erect smelters where the ores dug up by others could be treated and the metals made ready for shipment to the great industrial centers farther east. He and several of his sons persisted, under real difficulties in the early days, in perfecting the metallurgical processes necessary for extracting at a profit the metals from very different ores, or concentrates, that came to them from the hills. Their success in the smelting and refining business was phenomenal, and their wealth led to notable public services, to the support of scientific research in aviation, and to the establishment of the Guggenheim Foundation which is devoted to the support of research, literature and the fine arts.

On certain of the specimens which Mr. Stratton secured in the Cripple Creek district and took to the assay office, he received reports of ore containing $380 worth of gold per ton. That clearly meant that he had discovered a bonanza. From 1891 to 1898, one of Mr. Stratton's mines, the Independence, was valued at $3,985,440, and the profit to him was $2,402,-164. From 1898 to 1904 the same mine produced metals worth $11,046,947, and paid dividends totaling $4,142,738. Altogether, the Independence Mine yielded $21,061,565 and paid dividends amounting to $7,393,654. Mr. Stratton died in 1901. Ten years had elapsed since his first important discoveries had been made on the slopes of Pikes Peak, and the Cripple Creek mining district had by that time produced about $125,000,000 in gold. From 1891 through 1940, this district produced gold worth $389,973,147.

LEADVILLE

No mining center in Colorado, and perhaps no other mining center in the Rocky Mountains, had a more sensational career than Leadville. The town was born in 1877 and was incorporated the next year. It is sometimes referred to as a city "that sprung up on the ashes of an old gold camp." When the Pikes Peak stampede of 1859 had proved a failure and the miners had become thoroughly disillusioned and disgusted with the peak and its precincts, some, who had no desire to return to their homes in the East, wandered westward into the interior mountain country of Colorado. Most of them kept at their work of sampling the stream gravels for placer gold, and some were very successful. Important discoveries were made on the west slope of the Park Range, near the site of Leadville, in what was called California Gulch. That name was given to the valley because it was thought that it might be as rich as some of the California gulches. At least five thousand men were at work there in 1861, and some of them made fairly good fortunes. It is estimated that they took gold dust worth at least $1,000,000 from the stream gravels of California Gulch in the first summer. Then the gold available in the gravel seemed to play out, and many of the men lost heart and wandered away. The camp dwindled and by 1867 it was nothing more than a ghost town.

A reawakening of the area came in 1874, when a heavy rock, which was causing some trouble in the operation of the sluice boxes, was called to the attention of Mr. William H. Stevens and one or two of his companions. That rock proved to be about one-quarter lead, and, in addition, to contain twenty dollars' worth of silver per ton. This discovery encouraged men to hunt over the hillsides for the mineral veins from which this rock came, and several locations were made on promising outcrops of vein material.

The real boom at Leadville began in 1878, when a very rich ore body was discovered in Fryer Hill, east of town. This begins with the story of August Rische, a shoemaker, and George Hook, one of his friends. They were both attracted to Leadville by the rumors of mineral wealth, but they were too poor to spend a whole season prospecting, and so they arranged with a storekeeper, Horace Tabor, to furnish them a "grubstake." That meant the storekeeper should have a right to 1/3 of anything they found. They located a claim, dug a shaft thirty feet deep, and struck a very rich body of ore. They called their mine the Little Pittsburg. By the end of the summer, Hook, wanting some ready cash, sold his rights to his partners for $98,000. Some banking men from Denver purchased Rische's interest in this and some other mines for $262,500. Tabor found other near-by claims which produced gold for him worth $1,500,000, and which he eventually sold for another $1,500,000.

Leadville by this time was a roaring mining camp. It had grown like a mushroom. Real estate which sold for one dollar per front foot soon jumped to one hundred and fifty dollars per front foot. Saloons came, quick-lunch stands were erected, dance halls, dives, gambling dens, and all that makes life lurid and hectic made their appearance. Gambling was wide open, and men lost fortunes more easily and in less time than they had made them. The Theatre Comique, which paid a rent of $1,700 per month, did a flourishing business. Fortunes were honestly made and fortunes were honorably lost in the mining ventures.

In 1877 there were probably two hundred people in the whole Leadville region and only a few log cabins; by 1880 the census listed 14,820 inhabitants. New mines were being continually opened up and developed. The hills were especially rich in silver ore, as well as in lead ore. In 1878, silver worth $2,000,000 was taken out of the near-by hills, and in the next year the hills produced $9,000,000 in silver alone. The ores at Leadville contain a large variety of metals, and the wealth produced is fabulous. The record for six metals from 1859 through 1940 is as follows:

Placer gold	$ 7,271,575
Lode gold	50,415,099
Silver	192,363,746
Copper	14,584,784
Lead	92,689,445
Zinc	95,254,850
Grand Total	$452,579,499

Horace Tabor, who grubstaked the two men who made some of the early discoveries of rich ore in the Leadville region, had a career that is typical of the early days. The mines and claims which he bought and sold brought him, for a time, great fortunes. He was very free with his money. He established a bank in Leadville, built a great opera house there, and in Denver erected the Tabor Grand Opera House, which he tried to make the most splendid showplace in the United States. He was very generous and established many philanthropic institutions. He served as a United States Senator for thirty days, but with the fall in the value of silver he was financially ruined. Late in his career he was awarded the postmastership in Denver, and in 1899 he died a poor man. His widow continued to live in Leadville, believing in the mines which had given them a great fortune, but in 1935 she died in poverty.

Many fantastic things happened in Leadville. About Christmas time in 1895, a most spectacular building was opened as a ballroom, skating rink, dining hall, and riding gallery. With the exception of a few roof trestles, the entire building was composed of blocks of ice; it was a crystal castle, 325 feet wide and 433 feet long. The walls of the ballroom were twenty feet thick. Heat was provided in the dressing rooms, the lighting was furnished by electricity, and in the center of the great pavilion rose imposing octagonal pillars, five feet in diameter, to support the roof. A cowboy band played for the skaters and dancers.

This crystal palace, with the architecture of a Norman castle, carried eight huge towers, mounting above the main walls to heights of forty-five, sixty, and ninety feet. Two massive pillars, measuring forty feet across and ninety feet high, stood planted on either side of the main entrance. The entrance itself was fronted with a masterpiece of ice carving in the form of the figure of a woman, entitled "Leadville," standing nineteen feet high and resting on a pedestal of ice twenty feet square. This great amusement hall, two miles above sea level, contained a merry-go-round and a toboggan slide and provided for ice yachting and sleighing as well as for dancing and skating. Undoubtedly a good deal of eating and drinking went on also.

THE SAN JUAN REGION

While all these discoveries and fortunes were made in the Leadville region, there was mining going on in the San Juans at a great rate. In the southwestern corner of Colorado, in the great structural dome which we have referred to over and over again in describing the origin and development of the

Rockies, many rich bodies of ore have been discovered. The volcanic events in the history of that range were very important in the concentration of the metals in certain veins, fissures, and shear zones. Ores are commonly in the great trunk channels of underground circulation, where heated waters, vapors, and gases, emanating from, or affected by, the hot rocks, mingle and where precipitation takes place. When a number of underground solutions become mixed, something is certain to be precipitated. If we took the contents of a dozen test tubes in a chemical laboratory, each containing a different substance in solution, and mixed them, we should almost certainly have a precipitate. So in nature's great chemical laboratory, with its water, gases, vapors, great heat, and changes in pressure, chemical changes take place. Certain porous rocks, or crushed areas or cracks, become mineralized, and, if the minerals are those which man desires and can extract at a profit, they are ores.

In the San Juan region most of the mines are centered about Ouray, Telluride, Silverton, Rico, and Creede. Durango and Ouray became smelting and outfitting centers. The mines are widely scattered. Some are in the very high portions of the mountains, 10,000 to 12,000 feet above the sea, where men become very nervous and tense if they remain too long; some are in the canyons. Many of the higher mines can be reached only by trail. They are perched on steep mountainsides, some on nearly vertical walls, almost anywhere that a rich mineral vein has been discovered. Some of the ores have been taken down on pack animals; others, by tramways, or on long belt conveyors. Electric light and power lines cross the high ranges to the great centers of activity, and telephones are installed at

226

most of the mines. Today many of the mines are active, and at places the tailings from the mills of earlier days are being reworked at a profit by modern processes.

The story of the Camp Bird Mines, near Ouray, may best serve our purpose. High among the mountains in the northwestern portion of the range, and at places accessible by trail from Silverton and Ouray, a number of very rich mineral veins were discovered. The men who were working there found ores that ran twelve to twenty dollars a ton in gold. The expense of carrying the ore on pack animals to Silverton for smelting and the cost of smelting made it impossible to get a profit unless the ore contained at least one hundred dollars' worth of metal per ton. These claims were 11,500 feet above sea level, in the volcanic rocks that formed the summit area in that part of the range.

Some of the mining men would not give up. They kept at it, doing at least their assessment work each year and making enough to pay their expenses. In 1896, Thomas F. Walsh, one of the spectacular figures in western mining history, became interested in these mining claims. Walsh, who was operating a smelter at Silverton, one day received certain interesting ores which he thought could be treated at a profit. He went into the high mountains and, by taking samples from several of the dumps around the workings of the prospectors, discovered the claims where the very rich ores must be located. He set to work buying up all abandoned claims on tax titles and several of the best mineral veins that had been opened up. He consolidated all of these properties and called them the Camp Bird Mines. By 1900 these properties had yielded a profit of

227

$1,650,000 and were valued at $6,000,000. Walsh sold a large share in the Camp Bird Mines to an English company for $5,000,000. He received $3,500,000 at once in cash, and before his death, in 1910, he obtained in royalties the balance due him. His share in the dividends was very large, and Walsh became one of the wealthy mining men of Colorado.

The Camp Bird Mill has been one of the show places of the San Juan Mountains. The ore was brought in buckets on a tramway for nearly two miles to a stamp mill, where it was crushed in a modern plant, and much of the free milling gold recovered on jig-tables. The balance of the crushed material was carried into a cyanide plant, where over ninety per cent of the gold content was recovered. In addition to gold, the ore contained silver, lead, and copper. During one month in 1910 the profit from the mine was a little over $150,000. According to a report published by the Camp Bird Company, the metallic content extracted from ores during the years 1902-16, inclusive, had a value of a little more than $23,000,000. In 1940 the mine declared no dividend.

There are lots of ups and downs in the mining business, and in the San Juan region, as in all other old mining districts, there are ghost towns. The ore bodies play out, or costs increase, or something happens that makes it impossible for anyone to make a profit in that region at mining. One by one the mining men move away with their families. Everyone who can, goes. The last to leave is usually an old prospector whose hopes are almost unquenchable. He gets someone to grubstake him, uses his neighbors' shacks as firewood, keeps a small kitchen garden, allows his beard to become long and shaggy, does a little min-

Moraine Lake in the Canadian Rockies.

Mt. Robson and Berg Lake near Jasper National Park.

Royal Gorge. This remarkable canyon was cut by the Arkansas River during its persistent fight to maintain its course across the Front Range.

ing on the richer claims, and is delighted to visit with anyone from the "outside." The town is dead.

THE RESURRECTION OF CENTRAL CITY

Soon after the Pikes Peak boom-fiasco, gold was discovered far back in the mountains west of Denver, 8,500 feet above sea level. The first claims staked off in 1859 were followed by so many more that by 1864 a settled community was established, large enough to be incorporated as Central City. It was for a time a rip-roaring mining center in the midst of many bonanza claims, where huge fortunes were made and lost. All of the color and excitement of a prosperous mining camp were present. When General Grant visited the town, a street was paved with silver bricks worth $12,000. By 1890 the population had increased to 2,480 and in 1900, to 3,114.

By the close of the gay nineties many substantial buildings of brick and stone had been erected. One was a large opera house on the main street of town, where Sarah Bernhardt, Modjeska, Booth, Joseph Jefferson and many other celebrated actors appeared before the miners and bonanza kings. For a time Central City enjoyed a great boom. Money came easily to many, and it was spent or lost at some gambling table just as easily.

After producing good returns for half a century, the ores began to play out. People drifted away. By 1910 the population was reduced to 1,782; by 1930, to 572. The place was nearly dead and was commonly referred to as a ghost town. Then came the resurrection. The descendants of its original

229

builder gave the opera house to the University of Denver. Someone who must have known the story of Salzburg, in the Austrian Alps, thought of making this old mining town, high among the mountains of Colorado, a center for a summer theater and the opera. The sixty-three-year-old stone building was refurbished, the hickory chairs restored, and the curtain went up on Lillian Gish in "Camille." Crowds came from near and far, and the town began to enjoy another season of prosperity. During 1941 the summer opera scheduled twenty-five performances. Throngs of people, many of whom had taken season tickets, crowded into Central City. All accommodations at the opera house were engaged. In that old ghost town among the mine-scarred mountains of Colorado more real grand opera was heard during that summer than in any other city in the United States. After the war is over and we can travel freely, this project should be revived.

THE GREAT DIAMOND FIASCO

Among the great stories of the Rocky Mountain region there is nothing more astounding, more shocking, more humiliating, and nothing more amusing than the diamond swindle of 1872. Two weather-beaten prospectors named Slack and Arnold, who seemed to be "simple-minded fellows" and were naturally unwilling to trust anyone with their "momentous secret," dropped in at the Bank of California one day, to deposit a bag of uncut diamonds and rubies for safekeeping. They estimated their treasures as worth $125,000 and said they had found them in "a desert portion of the West."

230

The men appeared rather indifferent about their discovery, although they were very careful not to tell where it was. The president of the bank and his associates, in a state of great excitement, wired to friends in London, and before long had Baron Rothschild very much interested in the great diamond discovery in the western part of the United States. The South African diamonds were just coming into the world markets, and many people were eager to invest in these precious stones and in the mining companies under organization for the control of the output and prices of such gems.

Slack and Arnold finally agreed to guide a small group to their claim, on condition that the men were blindfolded during the last part of the journey, and again on leaving the location. The first visit was carried out in that way, and men experienced in mining went into the region with the original discoverers of the claim, examined the property, did some washing of the gravels, and brought back with them a considerable number of diamonds. They also brought back rubies, emeralds, sapphires, and amethysts—gems about which they might well have been suspicious, for that is an almost impossible association. All these gems come from very different rock formations, and have never all been found closely associated in one small area. Some of the diamonds which were displayed in San Francisco created tremendous interest, and hundreds of people wanted to buy stock in the new venture. One of those diamonds was sent to Tiffany, the famous New York jeweler, who declared the gem to be worth $150,000. At that time few people in this country knew how to judge uncut diamonds accurately.

In order to be very careful and businesslike, the wealthy

men of San Francisco, who were interested in gaining control of this discovery of diamonds, employed a distinguished mining engineer, a man with an excellent reputation, to make a report on the property. He went with Slack and Arnold to the area, not knowing that he was but a few miles south of the Wyoming line in Colorado. Slack and Arnold took the party in by a zigzag route. After a few days, one of the members of the party complained of feeling ill and demanded that he be taken out of the region. That hurried the mining expert in his examination. He had spent much of his time surveying the limits of the claims to be staked off and had very little left for sampling the property. Slack and Arnold helped him to search for diamonds, assisted him in washing the gravels and in panning those gravels in order to reclaim the gems that were there. They actually did much of the panning themselves. That was clever, for they could easily "salt" the pan. They allowed the expert to find several diamonds.

Upon their return to San Francisco, the mining engineer made his report to the men who had engaged him and recommended that the purchase be made at $4,000,000, which he considered a safe and attractive proposition. Plans for a company were drawn up. Twenty-five men were allowed to share in the venture and together they immediately raised $2,000,-000. The company was capitalized at $10,000,000 but fortunately no stock was offered for sale to the public.

The sensational story of the diamonds spread like wildfire to all mining camps and to all big investment centers. A group of United States geologists, under the direction of Clarence King, who were at the time making a survey along the 40th

Parallel, heard of the diamond-hunting parties and visited the locality. They examined the soils carefully, the footprints, and the distribution of gems, and made many tests of the sands and gravels for diamonds. They found some fragments of diamonds and, interestingly enough, found fragments that had been cut artificially. Those fragments did not have the natural crystal forms of a diamond, but surfaces common to all commercial diamonds cut especially for reflecting and refracting light. It was clear that the material scattered about on the surface of the land was chiefly waste or scrap fragments from a diamond-cutting establishment. There was absolutely no wealth in the ground below the surface. The underlying rocks were not of a character to lead anyone to expect to find such an array of precious stones. The whole thing looked absurd.

Mr. King took men into the region where the claims were staked off. It was clear that the soil had been worked over, that the diamonds were all at, or near, the surface, and that emeralds, sapphires, rubies, and amethysts were scattered promiscuously over the surface. It was later brought out that Slack and Arnold had bought for $8,500 a considerable quantity of more or less waste material from a diamond cutter in London and brought the material to this country.*

It is reported that the two "simple-minded, weather-beaten prospectors" received a payment of approximately $600,000 for their interests, and it is claimed that the material which they used in "salting" the claim must have cost about $35,500.

* An exposure was published in detail in *The Engineering and Mining Journal*, December 10, 1872.

Those figures do not check with the investment made by them in London, but wild stories are told of this great venture. One statement, which may be correct, is that they received a final cash payment of $300,000. Slack, it appears, received $30,000. Arnold had the bulk of the returns, and he went to Kentucky to live quietly and very comfortably among some of his good friends. When the swindle had been completely aired, the $2,000,000 which had been paid in by the twenty-five men was returned to them, and the president of the bank, who had purchased the property from Slack and Arnold and who had been one of the chief promoters of this venture, took his loss. Arnold was sued for perpetrating this terrible fraud, but his townspeople thought he was a fine fellow and supported him at the trial. In the end, he paid $150,000 to the complainants, with the understanding that he would be entirely free from any further litigation or charges in connection with the fiasco. Less than one year after this settlement was made, he died.

THE BLACK HILLS

Among the dark, pine-covered hills of South Dakota that rise conspicuously above the Great Plains, there were Indians who long ago knew how and where to find gold. They had discovered it in the gravels of some stream courses and they had done a little placer mining. The Black Hills region was a good hunting ground in the early days; it provided an abundance of firewood and timber, and its streams offered a plentiful supply of fish. Furthermore, it gave them gold, which

234

could be used in trading with the white men. Hence the Indian people were very jealous of the area.

As white people came pressing westward in this country, in the seventies of the last century, reports reached them of the placer gold among the Black Hills. Some ventured into the Indian lands. There was trouble and considerable bloodshed. Several years passed before the United States Government made a settlement with the Indians, persuading them to accept another area as a reservation and to turn over the Black Hills to the white people. About 1876 a stampede of miners reached this part of the new West. They took a few hundred thousand dollars' worth of metal from the gold and tin placers. Then lode mining began. Prospectors discovered veins on the hillsides that contained free gold, which could be reclaimed in stamp mills.

George Hearst, whom we remember as one of the purchasers of the richest mine at Butte, took an option on the Homestake Mine at $70,000 and later was one of the purchasers of that mine, the richest in the Black Hills district. By 1878 the Homestake Mining Company had an eighty-stamp mill set up and was beginning to make large profits from the ore taken from a huge, open pit, where they were working from the surface downward on a richly mineralized zone near the north end of the Black Hills. In those days the ores contained about ten dollars' worth of metals per ton. The milling processes were being perfected, and in 1879 the men reclaimed an average of $9.69 worth of metal from every ton of ore. The profits were becoming very attractive.

235

The sinking of deep shafts thousands of feet into the ground followed the open-cut mining of the early days. Larger mills were built. The company soon had a thousand stamps crushing the ore, and each stamp crushed about four tons a day. Four thousand tons of ore passed each day through improved processes for extracting gold and other metals from the rock material. Cyanide plants were built, the flotation method was used for reclaiming lead, and little by little the company found it possible to work lower and lower grades of ore at a profit. In 1894 their mills yielded $1,390,610 in the value of metals extracted from the ore. Later, as the processes grew more refined and perfected, the company succeeded in extracting between ninety and ninety-five per cent of the values found by careful assay processes. For more than thirty years huge quantities of ore have been taken from that mine, high wages have been paid, and the freight rates have been high. Nevertheless, through skill and efficiency, the company had paid, by 1912, to those who had risked their savings in this venture, $27,000,000 in dividends.

In 1929 development work had reached a depth of 2,600 feet, and that year the dividends amounted to $1,758,120. Since then, the value of the ore has amounted to about $6,000,000 a year, and the yearly dividends have been about $1,750,000. There are huge reserves of ore deep in the ground; over 15,000,000 tons have been blocked out. The total production up to 1931 was over 59,000,000 tons, and the dividends up to that time amounted to more than $57,000,000—or about one dollar per ton of ore mined.

So runs the story of the bonanza days. New discoveries are

possible. Great mining may come again to the region. But the days of easy exploration are gone. Many of the lively camps are now mere shadows of towns, pitiful wrecks of past glory. Mining in the Rocky Mountain region has lost its gamble. Today it is a scientific and carefully planned business venture.

CHAPTER TWELVE

INDIANS, RANCHMEN, FARMERS, AND TOURISTS

The first people, as far as we know, to live near or in the area of the Rocky Mountains were the so-called American Indians. They came presumably from Asia by way of Alaska, with the culture of the Stone Age, and spread southward and eastward, making their living by hunting, fishing, and collecting. With spears and arrows, tipped with points of quartz or obsidian, they became very skillful hunters. On the plains east of the mountains they found thousands of buffalo and they preyed upon those animals for food and for robes to put on the floors of their tepees. In the mountain area they found deer, antelope, elk, moose, bear, rabbits, and many small animals they could kill. The streams abounded in fish, and the Indians became very skillful with spears and nets in securing the fish. The shrubbery in the mountain valleys provided berries in abundance each season. High among the mountains the blueberries flourished; in the lower places raspberries, blackberries, and wild cranberries were found. With all this, plenty of wood in the forests, and pure, clear water from mountain

241

streams those people had a delightful opportunity to live a camping sort of existence.

From their legends it appears clear that the Indians thought of the mountains as the great pillars that held up the skies, where mighty beings lived who spoke through the thunder and revealed themselves by flashes of lightning. There are stories that tell of the great blue arch of the heavens supported by the rainbow. Some tribes believed the mountains to be the Abode of the Souls, reached only by those adventurous spirits who could run the gauntlet of terrible snow storms, torrents, falling rocks, and perilous bridges.

There was a belief among some of the Indians of this area that long ago one of their men was told in a dream of vast wealth hidden upon a mountain top. He went in quest of this wealth and when he found it, in his greed, he took all, leaving nothing as an offering to the mountain. This resulted in great anger on the part of the mountain, which shook, smoked, and belched forth fire. The man was so terrified that he threw down his riches—and fell dead upon the spot where he had been standing. When he awoke, he was in his own camp.

Among the Shoshoni there was the legend that the firmament was a great dome of ice against which the rainbow, a huge serpent, rubbed its back. The friction caused by this action broke off pieces of ice, which in winter fell to the ground as snow and in the summer, as rain. They ascribed the thunder to the howling of coyotes, while others among them believed that thunder was due to a celestial mouse running over the clouds.

The mountains were always places of revelation sought out by the medicine men and prophets of the Indian peoples; there those mystic doctors kept solitary vigils in the lodges of the Gods, learning of mysteries which would help them in bringing salvation to their people.

The early dwellers among the mountains are represented today by various small Indian tribes. The Shoshoni are in Idaho, the Blackfeet in Montana. On the south side of the Uinta Mountains dwell the northern Utes, and their southern cousins make their home in southwestern Colorado and nearby states.

The American Indians were not entirely nomadic. They lived a sedentary life most of the time, having villages or well established camps. In those homes they learned the arts of pottery and basketry, and some became skillful weavers who made excellent blankets. The Navajo do not frequent the mountains very much now. They live in the plateau region southwest of the mountains of Colorado. They are the great blanket makers and silversmiths of modern times. Other groups are found in Central Wyoming just west of Lander. There they carry on many of their ancient customs and ceremonies.

The Indian peoples were not altogether friendly to the first white people who ventured into their hunting grounds and homelands but they have become adjusted to the presence of the intruders. Today the Indians profit very largely by the aid of the national government and from various opportunities for work provided by the white people who have come to live in the mountain area.

Our field studies in the mountains have brought us into close association with many of these Indian peoples. We never had any serious trouble with them. They are kindly and respond very quickly to a friendly attitude, and they are particularly pleased with little presents you may give them.

Mountain Sheep was one of the leading men of the northern Utes some years ago, and I remember his coming into our camp one evening about suppertime. He was undoubtedly curious as well as hungry. He probably wanted to know what we were doing on Indian lands and he may have thought we were prospectors. If men found mineral wealth on their reservation, the Indians feared that, through an act of Congress, some of their land might be taken away from them and a mining enterprise established. It was our habit to keep our prospecting picks out of sight while working in the Indian reservations, for we did not want them to be unfriendly to us. Even if they did no harm to us personally, they might run our horses off at night and in that way cause considerable trouble, delaying us in our work.

When the old chief arrived in our camp that evening, I was making the biscuits, and Mrs. Atwood, who was with me that season, was placing the dishes on a canvas that served as a tablecloth. Mountain Sheep watched us. In a few minutes he grunted a very deep grunt and said, "She your squaw?" and I said, "Yes." In a few moments, after another grunt, he said, "She Mormon squaw?" I said, "Oh no, I brought her from the East; she no Mormon squaw." A third grunt came just as I was putting the biscuits in the reflector oven and he said, "Your squaw heap tired." After supper he rode off with a broad smile on his face.

Several months later Mountain Sheep brought into camp one of his favorite saddle horses, a beautiful black stallion,

244

and I remember asking if I could have a ride. He granted me that privilege but told me not to lean forward. After getting a little used to the pony I thought I would disobey his injunction and, leaning forward a bit, I watched to see what would happen. Away went the black beauty like the wind. He started with a mighty jump and ran like a wild animal. In a few minutes I had all I wanted of that and, straightening up, I reined him in to a reasonable speed. Mountain Sheep enjoyed my experience and needed very little urging to stay with us again for supper. I saw him several times in later seasons while at work in the mountains near his home, and he always chuckled about my squaw and about my ride on his little black pony. He was always our friend.

Long after the Indians had established their homes in the region of the Rocky Mountains there came white people from the south and east. A few parties of Spanish explorers ventured into the southern portion of the mountain area in what is now New Mexico and Colorado. Coranado, while searching for the fabled "Seven cities of Cibola," is believed to have entered the Colorado territory in 1540. Santa Fé, New Mexico, the second oldest city in the United States, was founded by the Spanish in 1609 and by 1630 had a population of 250 Spaniards, about 700 Indians and a few half-breeds. Many Spanish explorers from settlements on the Rio Grande ventured into the mountains of Colorado. Some prospected for gold on the banks of the San Juan River. Others pushed on westward and southwestward to the Pacific coastal lands.

In 1805 the Lewis and Clarke expedition moving northwest-

245

ward near the valley of the Missouri River reached the Rocky Mountains in the present state of Montana. Those adventurous fellows advanced into the high mountain region, passing westward near the site of Three Forks, where the Madison, Jefferson, and Gallatin Rivers unite and form the Missouri River. On their return journey in 1806 they crossed the Rockies again. In that same year, 1806, Zebulon M. Pike, while making a map of the Arkansas and Red Rivers in the region of the Great Plains—east of the mountains—followed the Arkansas into Colorado and discovered the famous peak which carries his name. Major S. H. Long, who is commemorated in the name of the highest peak in the Rocky Mountain National Park, visited this western country in 1819-1820.

Trappers and fur traders were among those who very early built cabins and trading stations in this mountain region. A few came to the site of Denver, in 1799. James Purcell, following the fur trade, entered the Colorado region in 1803. For the next half century fur trading predominated in much of the Rocky Mountain area. And next came the prospectors to whom we referred in the last chapter.

After the first gold rushes took place, the great westward trek began. As the mining towns increased in number and in population, as smelters, furnaces, and crushing mills multiplied, as metropolitan centers of trading, banking, and manufacture became more numerous, the local demands for food increased. Some of those who were drifting westward and some who had tried their luck at mining, without any great success, turned to ranch life or farming.

246

The Great Plains to the east of the mountains had long been recognized as excellent pasturelands. Where the buffalo once roamed by the thousands, large cattle ranches had been established. For a long time most of the pastureland of the "West" was unfenced and served as an open range, free for anyone to use. Each ranchman had a string of cowboys, whose duty it was to keep his cattle located where there was good grass and to see to it that all of his calves were properly branded.

Pressure of population on the land continued to increase, railroads extended their tracks westward, more and more of the Great Plains was fenced, and many of the ranchmen were forced to look for new pastures. At first they did not like the idea of taking their cattle into the high mountains. It was all right for sheep to be pastured in the alpine meadows, but, in their judgment, that was no place for cattle. They held that the season was too short, that the steers wouldn't have a chance to get over the effects of the long drive in before winter would run them out. The country was too high for cattle; there were high-altitude diseases that would kill the steers. The larkspur would poison the animals. For a long time the cowpunchers refused to believe that the mountain pastures were any good for their stock.

However, after years of hesitation, group after group of ranchmen did move into the mountain valleys, and to their surprise found the climate much more agreeable than that of the Great Plains region. The water supply was excellent, the grass was more nutritious, and the larkspur menace could be overcome. Slowly but certainly, the high-altitude bogey was so completely overcome that the cattlemen held that the mountain pastures produced some of the very best grades of beef. They came to believe that grazing conditions over most of the mountain areas, where there was a good rainfall, were superior to those in the semiarid regions of the Great Plains.

For many years the men who specialized in cattle and those who were primarily interested in sheep were in fierce competition for the best pastures on the government-owned lands of the West. They organized opposing camps, or bands, established "dead lines," and actually killed each other's livestock when the offending animals were found in forbidden territory. Thousands of sheep were killed—sometimes with clubs—to save the expense of ammunition; cattle were shot, and the owners of the cattle and the sheep became bitter enemies. The cattlemen claimed that the feeding grounds for the sheep must be limited and defined, for the cattle would not graze where sheep had been pastured. Each group held that the other was making life impossible for them and their families, because their animals were starving to death. Old-timers in the mountain country recall many a battle, fought with clubs or with guns, in the field or in town, when rival ranchmen came face to face. This kind of trouble was largely removed by the establishment of our national forests and the assignment of pastures to the various ranchmen.

Among the settlers who wished to establish permanent homes among the mountains, there were those who were quick to pre-empt the more fertile parts of the valley lowlands for farmlands. They took advantage of the Homestead Acts to select attractive places near the stream courses where, if necessary, irrigation could be practiced. Fields were located where fodder crops, such as alfalfa, beans, peas, and oats for winter feeding could be produced. These settlers planned to combine agriculture and ranching as livestock farmers. Those who kept both cattle and sheep held the cattle in the open pastures within the forested areas during the summer seasons, and drove the sheep into the alpine areas above the tree line, where the grasses and shrubs are luxuriant during the warmer three months of the year. When fall came, the herders and cowboys brought the sheep and cattle out of the mountains and pastured them near the ranch homes. In that way the system of seasonal migration for animal pasture, common to many of the mountain regions of the world, was established in our western mountains.

PASTURES IN THE NATIONAL FORESTS

As the movement of conservation gained headway in our country, under the able leadership of Theodore Roosevelt, more and more of the forested areas among the mountains were set aside as national reservations. There are now 130,538 square miles in the national forests of the Rocky Mountain states. Many of the mountainsides are too steep for the plow. If left forested, they can be made to provide a permanent supply of timber; furthermore, the forests will prevent disastrous floods. Among the trees and in the many open places in a forest, there is usually sufficient grass to provide good pasturage for stock.

In the administration of our national forests a reasonable amount of grazing is permitted, and each near-by ranchman is assigned pastureland suitable for the number and kind of animals he wishes to place in the forest. The areas most suitable for cattle are reserved for them, those best adapted for grazing sheep are held for that purpose. Careful supervision of the range lands prevents overgrazing, reduces soil erosion, and makes the pastures available for the ranchmen year after year. Since the livestock farmers pay a board bill for each animal pastured in the national forests, there is considerable income from this source, which is used in support of the forest service.

The mountain pastures may be divided into five different zones. Around the base of each range there is a lower, or transition, zone in which, very commonly, there are yellow pines. There the forest is open, and varieties of bunch grass are available for the livestock. The next higher zone is characterized by the lodgepole pine and aspens. These trees grow so close together in some areas that they prevent the growth of grasses, but in most sections there are open treeless patches with good grasses. The third zone begins at about 6,500 feet above sea level. It is characterized by the whitebark pine and fir. It is cooler and not available for livestock as early in the season as the lower zones. The trees are in small groves, and there are extensive open meadows with bunch grasses. The fourth and still higher zone is above the tree line. There we find the alpine meadows with some small shrubs that provide ideal pasturelands for sheep. The fifth zone includes the rocky summit regions in the mountains. Though it does not have much grass, you will sometimes see domestic sheep that have wandered high above the alpine meadows nibbling at whatever grows in the cracks between the rocks. The wild mountain sheep and mountain goats make their living in this zone.

CATTLE ROUNDUPS

Most ranchmen found it advisable to have two roundups each year. In the fall the cowboys of a grazing district, riding far and wide on the range, brought all the cattle they could find together, and then the animals were separated into groups according to their brands. Each ranchman picked out the marketable beef in his herd, and the selected animals were then driven to the nearest shipping center, where they were consigned to some one of the large packing houses in Omaha, Kansas City, Chicago, Cincinnati, or some other city to the eastward. Another group of younger animals was picked out for feeding on the home farm, or on farms in the corn belt. Thousands of them were sent into Iowa, northern Missouri, Illinois, or Indiana. Feeding cattle can be carried out at considerable profit. In Colorado the ranchmen figured that beef can be fattened for market at a profit of from ten to twenty dollars a head. Two- or three-year-old steers are finished off in about 120 to 150 days; yearlings in about 160 days; calves must be fed, usually, for six or seven months.

At the ranches, alfalfa hay forms the backbone of cattle feed for market. Pea vines, bean straw, cane, Sudan hay and, in the southerly areas, pea fields are used in feeding livestock. Barley and corn are also raised by some of the ranchmen for feeding purposes. After sugar beets have been crushed for their sugar content, the pulp, which is left, is used as a by-

251

product in fattening cattle. In an average year, under normal conditions of the market, Colorado fattens and sends east about 140,000 cattle. Each of the Rocky Mountain states produces a large number of beef cattle every year.

In the spring another roundup is held. This time it is to brand the calves. When that has been done, the animals are all driven off to their summer pasturelands, which are usually in national forests. Many of the ranchmen located in the mountain area have homes conveniently situated at the margin of some great national reservation, where they can arrange to pasture their stock.

The roundups of early days were great social occasions, for the young people from widely scattered ranches came together at these times for sports and a thrilling type of celebration, featuring horse races, broncobusting, bulldozing, roping, branding, and all sorts of contests. The old-fashioned roundups are the ancestors of the modern rodeos of "Pioneers' Day," "Frontier Day," and of the wild West shows that travel over the country.

MILLIONS OF POUNDS OF WOOL

The story of the care of sheep is somewhat different. Every spring, after the lambing period is over, the wool from the older sheep must be clipped and baled for shipment east. From Colorado alone about 9,000,000 pounds of wool are shipped eastward annually. After the shearing is completed, each band of sheep must be "dipped." The animals are forced into a

252

trough partly filled with a solution of chemicals. When they dive in they are completely covered and as they run through the trough they become well soaked with the fluid which should cure or prevent any skin diseases. Then they start overland in great herds along routes which have been selected and marked as "stock driveways" through the forest to meadows high in the mountains above the tree line. There they feast in rich summer pastures, which would otherwise be of little or no economic use.

In the clear, fresh air, among snow-capped summits, the shepherds live with their sheep throughout the summer months. For weeks at a time their only companions are two or three shepherd dogs that help them in rounding up the sheep on the bedding ground each evening. The dogs are more or less alert all through the night, so that the approach of bears, coyotes, or wolves may be announced to the herder.

At the bedding ground for the sheep, the shepherd prepares a hollowed-out log to serve as a trough for the salt which the sheep must have. Near by is the little tent where he and his dogs sleep. There he prepares his simple meals day after day through the summer season, eating them in utter solitude. His life is unbelievably monotonous. Some sheep owners arrange to send a man to each of their bands with salt and provisions once in two or three weeks. He comes as a most welcome guest, both for his companionship and for his help to the shepherds in moving camp to new pastures.

In Montana there are upwards of 6,000,000 sheep in the mountains and in the neighboring basin lands. In Colorado

253

3,000,000 are reported on the ranges and ranches. Sheep are produced in large numbers in each of the Rocky Mountain states. From the standpoint of the stockman, flexibility is very important in this enterprise. Production should be increased when the prices are high and reduced when prices are low. Every owner of sheep must watch the national and international markets. The prices he receives for his mutton, wool, and skins may depend on the production of sheep in Australia, Argentina, or in any one of the great pasturelands of the world where a surplus is produced and offered for sale in the competitive market.

In each band of sheep sent into the mountains the economic unit is from 1,800 to 2,200 head. Alfalfa, corn, barley, oats, beet pulp, and cane silage are used in fattening the lambs for market. On the average a farmer will feed from 900 to 2,500 lambs each year, and he expects as a profit from one to two dollars a head.

COWBOY SONGS

The cowboy is the most romantic of the frontiersmen. His life in the open, roping cattle, branding calves, breaking broncos, camping out for weeks at a time away from the home ranch, present endless tests in endurance, co-operation, patience, and good-fellowship. There were many long, lonely rides for those fellows in the early days, and, to pass the time, as their saddle horses jogged along the trails, they took to singing. Naturally, their songs pictured their own surroundings, experiences, and emotions.

Home, home on the range
Where the deer and the antelope play;
Where seldom is heard a discouraging word
And the skies are not cloudy all day.

Often, when we were gathered about the campfire, these true westerners, who had actually punched and branded cattle, would get together—sometimes lying on their backs—and begin to sing very softly. The rhythm always suggested the jogging of cow ponies on the trail or on the lone prairie. Many of the songs had a touch of pathos, reflecting homesickness, a desire to see mother or some fair maiden. One I remember told of the sad ending of a fine fellow thrown from his saddle far from camp. I have heard these songs so many times that I can repeat many of the verses from memory. Where I needed help, my daughter came to the rescue. She learned all the songs around the campfire from the cowboys who were our helpers. They are put down here as our own boys sang them.

THE HORSE WRANGLER *

One day I thought I'd have some fun,
And see how punching cows was done;
So, when the round-up had begun
I tackled the cattle king.
Says he: "My foreman's gone to town;
He's in a saloon and his name is Brown.
If you see him, he'll take you down."
Says I, "That's just the thing."

* The cowboy songs are published with the permission of John Lomax, Alan Lomax, and the Macmillan Company.

We started for the ranch next day;
Brown argered me most all the way.
He said that cow-punching was nothing but play,
That it was no work at all,—
That all you had to do was ride,
'Twas only drifting with the tide;
The son of a gun, oh, how he lied!
Don't you think he had his gall?

He put me in charge of the cavyard,
And told me not to work too hard,
That all I had to do was guard
The horses from getting away;
I had one hundred and sixty head,
I sometimes wished that I was dead;
When one got away, Brown's head turned red,
And there was the Devil to pay.

Sometimes one would make a break,
Across the prairies he would take,
As if running for a stake,—
It seemed to them but play;
Sometimes I could not head them all,
Sometimes my horse would catch a fall
And I'd shoot on like a cannon ball
Till the earth came in my way.

They saddled me up an old gray hack
With two set fasts on his back,
They padded him down with a gunny sack
And used my bedding all.
When I got on he quit the ground,
Went up in the air and turned around,
And I came down and busted the ground,—
I got one hell of a fall.

They took me up and carried me in
And rubbed me down with an old stake pin.
"That's the way they all begin;
You're doing well," says Brown.
"And in the morning, if you don't die,
I'll give you another horse to try."
"Oh, say, can't I walk?" says I.
Says he, "Yes, back to town."

I've traveled up and I've traveled down,
I've traveled this country round and round,
I've lived in city and I've lived in town,
But I've got this much to say:
Before you try cow-punching, kiss your wife,
Take a heavy insurance on your life,
Then cut your throat with a barlow knife—
For it's easier done that way.

THE DYING COWBOY

"Oh, bury me not on the lone prairie."
These words came low and mournfully
From the pallid lips of a youth who lay
On his dying bed at the close of day.

"Oh, bury me not on the lone prairie
Where the wild coyotes will howl o'er me,
In a narrow grave just six by three
Oh, bury me not on the lone prairie.

"It matters not, I've oft been told,
Where the body lies when the heart grows cold;
Yet grant, oh, grant this wish to me:
Oh, bury me not on the lone prairie

"I've always wished to be laid when I died,
In the little churchyard on the green hillside;
By my father's grave there let mine be,
Oh, bury me not on the lone prairie!

"There is another whose tears may be shed
For one who lies on a prairie bed;
It pained me then and it pains me now—
She has curled these locks, she has kissed this brow.

"These locks she has curled; shall the rattlesnake kiss?
This brow she has kissed; shall the cold grave press?
For the sake of the loved ones that will weep for me,
Oh, bury me not on the lone prairie.

"Oh, bury me not—" and his voice failed there.
But we took no heed of his dying prayer;
In a narrow grave just six by three
We buried him there on the lone prairie.

And the cowboys now as they roam the plain—
For they marked the spot where his bones were lain—
Fling a handful of roses o'er his grave,
With a prayer to Him who his soul will save.

THE DYING RANGER

The sun was sinking in the west and fell with lingering ray
Through the branches of a forest where a wounded ranger lay;
'Neath the shade of a palmetto and the sunset silvery sky,
Far away from his home in Texas they laid him down to die.

A group had gathered round him, his comrades in the fight,
A tear rolled down each manly cheek as he bid a last good night.
258

One tried and true companion was kneeling by his side,
To stop his life-blood flowing; but, alas, in vain he tried.

"Draw closer to me, comrades, and listen to what I say:
I am going to tell a story while my spirit hastens away,
Way back in northwest Texas, that good old Lone Star State,
There is one that for my coming with a weary heart will wait.

"A fair young girl, my sister, my only joy, my pride,
She was my friend since boyhood; I have no one left beside.
I have loved her as a brother, and with a father's care
I have strove from grief and sorrow her gentle heart to spare.

"It is true I love my country; for her I gave my all.
If it hadn't been for my sister, I would be content to fall.
I am dying, comrades, dying; she will never see me more,
But in vain she'll wait my coming by our little cabin door.

"Comrades, gather closer and listen to my dying prayer.
Who will be to her as a brother, and shield her with a brother's care?"
Up spake the noble rangers, they answered one and all,
"We will be to her as brothers till the last one does fall."

One glad smile of pleasure o'er the ranger's face was spread;
One dark, convulsive shadow, and the ranger boy was dead.
Far from his darling sister we laid him down to rest
With his saddle for a pillow and his rifle across his breast.

UTAH CARROLL

And as, my friend, you ask me what makes me sad and still,
And why my brow is darkened like the clouds upon the hill;
Run in your pony closer and I'll tell to you the tale
Of Utah Carroll, my pardner, and his last ride on the trail.

'Mid cactus and the thistles of Mexico's fair land,
Where the cattle roam in thousands, a-many a herd and brand,
There is a grave with neither headstone, neither date nor name—
There lies my pardner, sleeping in the land from which I came.

Side by side we've rode the ranges, cut out, roped and burned the brand,
And through the storm and dreary darkness joined the night-herd's
    weary stand.
We rode the range together and had rode it side by side;
I loved him as a brother; I wept when Utah died.

We were rounding up one morning, our work was almost done,
When on the side the cattle started on a mad and fearless run;
The boss man's little daughter was riding on that side—
Started in to turn the cattle—it was there my pardner died.

Lenore rushed on her pony, tried to turn the cattle right;
Her red blanket slipped from beneath her, catching in her stirrup tight;
When we all saw the blanket, we gasped and held our breath,
For now should her pony fail her, naught could save the girl from
    death.

There is nothing on the ranges that will cause the cows to fight
Half so quick as some red object when it's waved before their sight;
When the cattle saw the blanket almost dragging on the ground
They were maddened in a moment and they charged it in a bound.

Then Lenore saw the threatening danger, quickly turned her pony's
    face,
And, in leaning from her saddle, tried her blanket to displace;
When she leaned she lost her balance, fell in front of this wild tide—
"Lie still, Lenore, I am coming!" were the words my pardner cried.

As the girl fell from her pony she had dragged the blanket down,
And it lay there close beside her as she lay upon the ground.

The Grand Tetons from the east. Several of the U-shaped troughs, formerly occupied by valley glaciers, are clearly shown on the front of the range.

Crystal Room in the Carlsbad Caverns. A wonderful display of delicate stalactites, which in a few places join with the crystalline forms rising from the floor.

The home of early people in Colorado. Cliff Palace in Mesa Verde National Park, where hundreds of cliff dwellers lived in a great cave under an overhanging layer of sandstone. The largest cliff dwelling in the world, with about three hundred separate rooms.

Cliff dwellings in Mesa Verde National Park.

Utah picked up the blanket. "Lie still," again he said,
Then he raced across the prairie and waved the blanket o'er his head.

As he ran across the prairie every cowboy gave a cry,
"He has saved the boss's daughter, though we know he's bound to die.
He has turned those maddened cattle from Lenore, his little friend!"
And now they rushed upon him and he stopped to play his hand.

Soon the cattle were upon him and my pardner had to fall,
Nevermore to cinch a bronco, nor to give a cattle call.
There he died upon the ranges, though it seemed most awful hard
That I could not make the distance in time to save my pard.

VALLEY RANCHES AND DUDE RANCHES

As settlements became much more numerous, as railroads
and highways were built in the Rocky Mountain area, general
farming was undertaken on most of the valley lowlands, in
the parks among the mountains, and at many places about the
margins of the mountains. Great irrigation projects were established; man-made oases sprang up at various places. In
some of the oases there are extensive orchards or truck farms.
Canning factories have been erected, and near some of the
large beet plantations there are great mills with crushing machinery and centrifugal bowls, where sugar is produced.

Some of the irrigation projects are financed by the Federal Government but others are co-operative enterprises entered into by farmers and ranchmen who need the water for
their lands during the latter part of the growing seasons.

One day, while at work in the San Juan Range with Kirt-

had been made was in not carefully examining the material to which the dam was tied. The water, when the pressure rose in the reservoir, soon found a way through that loose material and was pouring out fifteen hundred feet below the dam.

This discovery, which I reported at once to the United States Geological Survey Office in Washington, led to orders for an examination of other reservoir sites and the sites of projected reservoirs for which funds were being collected from the farmers and ranchmen in the San Luis Valley east of the mountains. The engineers were having trouble with the next reservoir I examined because the water was flowing around the dam through what they thought was solid rock. Again hundreds of thousands of dollars had been spent in the con-structional work, but the dam had been tied to a landslide rock. All one needed to do was to look at the mountain slope, just above the dam, to see the great scar indicating that a huge mass had slid down the mountainside and had lodged in the valley, thus creating the narrow place which, to the engineer, looked attractive for the location of a dam. But land-slide material is broken, crushed, and fragmental, and there are scores of waterways through such a mass which has come a thousand feet down the mountain with a great crash. Again the narrow place in the stream course had attracted the prac-tical engineer, for there he would not need a very large dam to hold the water. Again the dam was perfectly good. It would hold water, but the material to which the dam was tied or at-tached would not hold water, and again a large portion of a million dollars was thrown away.

I visited half a dozen such reservoirs. At each one of them

263

loose deposits, which are common to many of the mountain canyons, had so nearly blocked the stream courses that the dam sites were placed at those very localities. And in each case those loose materials were causing the loss of all the water or a large part of the water which the engineers had hoped to hold in the reservoir above the dam.

I came to one site where the constructional work had not yet been done and there discovered that the plans, which were all drawn up and made public by the promoters of this enterprise, involved the construction of a dam between a landslide mass on one side and a loose glacial deposit on the other. What a terrible mistake could have been made! The men might have built a perfectly good dam but there was little likelihood that those loose fragmental deposits, to which the dam was to be tied, would hold water. I condemned that site, and the dam was never built. The farmers and ranchmen did not lose their money. The director of the Survey, in a very cordial letter, told me that those few days of work had saved more money for the people of Colorado than the fifteen years of surveying which I had done in the mountains—at public expense—had cost the United States Government. A bulletin of but thirty-eight pages—the smallest report I ever had published by the Survey—in which I set forth all my findings, was issued and widely distributed. Perhaps it has done more good from a practical point of view than any of the longer reports setting forth the results of years of scientific field studies in the mountains.

The significance of all this is that no engineer, dealing with

264

the outdoor problems in a mountain region, should be without some geological field training or, before a final decision is made, he should engage a geologist to pass on any site he proposes to use for the location of a dam.

In almost every mountain canyon a favorable location can be found, with the canyon walls near together, where the stream can be dammed. At one side and just below the dam a power plant is erected. In that plant the falling water rotates huge turbines, and in the electric generators the power represented in those whirling wheels is transformed so that it can be sent over wires. Power lines follow the stream courses, cross over mountain ranges, go anywhere electricity is wanted. The whole mountain region is now electrified. Kitchens, dairy barns, creameries, sugar mills, crushing plants at the mines, the mines themselves, the city streets, homes, office buildings, city trolley lines and even some of the transcontinental railways are equipped with modern means for using hydro-electric power that comes from the mountains.

TOURIST AND VACATIONLAND

Today the Rocky Mountain portions of our country and of Canada are known to millions of people as regions in which to spend a happy vacation. In the national forests and in the national parks there are thousands of places where camping is permitted. Cabin camps are located at convenient intervals along the automobile highways, and in each of the parks near sites of special scenic or scientific interest. Many people have

265

built summer homes in the national forests. They return to those homes year after year and plan to pass them on to their children.

Licensed operators maintain cabin camps, lodges, and hotels in the national parks. There are all grades of accommodations in the parks, including the crudest of camp grounds, where firewood and water are available and you provide the rest; housekeeping cabins that are well furnished and have dishes, stoves, and refrigerators; de luxe cabins with innerspring mattresses, open fireplaces, easy chairs, radios, and all the comforts of home; cafeterias and great hotels, or châteaux, with all the extravagant conveniences of conventional city life.

Boys' camps, girls' camps, dude camps, and the good old-fashioned ranch which will take in a few boarders are maintained in or near the national forests, to help accommodate the tourist visitors and vacationists. Saddle horses, pack animals, and guides are available for those who wish to explore in the wilder portions, or climb to the summit areas of the mountain ranges. The annual tourist business during normal times probably brings more money into the mountain area than the mineral wealth taken out each year will produce. The mountains are providing recreation and inspiration for millions of people each year, combined with unequaled educational opportunities in many of the natural sciences. Perhaps in the end the greatest worth to the nation of this mountain region may prove to be in its esthetic and cultural values.

So the great range of the Rockies calls to the nation. There is a certain type of Rocky Mountain fever that is harmless, a mere summer-time recurring of a hunger to set up camp once again in a grove of aspens, a desire again to stand amid pristine beauty. There is something essentially salutary about the Rockies. Life comes to have great dignity, and the spirit repairs scars of the urban winter.

The Rockies rank among the greatest of the world ranges. They run from our southwest desert to the barren desert of northern Alaska. In this range there is every type of alpine vacation land, everything from de luxe dude ranches to lonely Canadian valleys open only to the experienced camper. Here is a country too great, too vast to be spoiled by vacationists. It is a land of splendor, dramatic purple shadows, icefields, brilliantly colored mountain slopes. Here is a land too little known, still awaiting the explorer. Its beauty is one of our great national heritages.

THE NATIONAL PARKS IN THE
ROCKY MOUNTAIN REGION

Within or very near the Rocky Mountains of the United States and Canada fourteen areas have been set aside, because of their special significance, as national parks. One, the Mesa Verde, is known chiefly for its historic or archaeological associations; the others are natural wonderlands of superb scenic beauty and of great scientific and inspirational value.

Beginning at the south and running northward, these parks include the following:

Carlsbad Caverns	in	New Mexico
Mesa Verde	"	Southwestern Colorado
Rocky Mountain	"	Colorado
Grand Teton	"	Wyoming
Yellowstone	"	Wyoming
Wind Cave	"	South Dakota
Glacier	"	Montana
Waterton Lakes	"	Alberta, Canada
Banff	"	Alberta, Canada
Jasper	"	Alberta, Canada
Kootenay	"	British Columbia, Canada
Yoho	"	British Columbia, Canada
Glacier	"	British Columbia, Canada
Mt. Revelstoke	"	British Columbia, Canada

There are also many national monuments in or near the Rocky Mountain region, so many that we cannot here describe them. They are similar to, though usually smaller than the parks. The National Park Service of the Department of the Interior will furnish information on all of these reservations to those who are interested. The capital city of Colorado has established a reservation in the Front Range of the Rockies, known as the Denver Mountain Park.

CARLSBAD CAVERNS NATIONAL PARK

About 1862, a group of cattlemen and goatherders, venturing underground in the hilly lands of New Mexico, not far from the Rocky Mountains, discovered a series of huge subterranean caverns, with remarkable crystalline formations hanging from the ceilings, and at places rising ten to fifteen feet from the floor. The men entered at a spot where the roof of a cave had collapsed, and found their way by candlelight from one chamber to another. They probably tied one end of a ball of twine at the entrance and unwound the string as they advanced into the maze of passageways in the pitch-dark underground, for they must have known that it is easy to get lost when exploring caves.

The rocky channels within the Carlsbad Caverns led the explorers to great holes, or pits, through which they descended to deeper and deeper levels, where they found other rooms and passageways. The caves at Carlsbad have been dissolved out of thick, nearly horizontal layers of limestone, hollowed

272

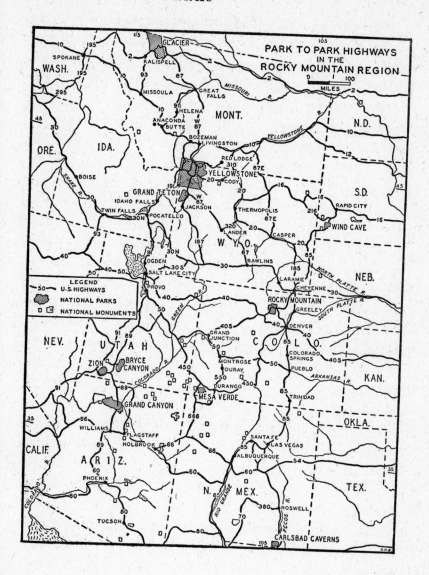

PARK TO PARK HIGHWAYS
IN THE
ROCKY MOUNTAIN REGION

273

into rooms ranging from twenty to fifty feet in height and from fifty to one hundred feet in diameter. They are all irregular in shape, and are connected by tunnels, or hallways, which the subterranean waters have dissolved out of the solid rock.

Little by little, more and more of the strange underground realm of darkness was penetrated, pictures were taken with flashlights, public interest was aroused, and in 1923, by an act of the United States Congress, the Carlsbad National Park was established. In normal times thousands of visitors are conducted through this mysterious wonderland each season. Well-trained ranger naturalists accompany the visitors and explain the remarkable crystalline formations in the caves. An elevator has been installed, which makes the return journey to the surface comparatively easy. In earlier days, visitors scrambled over a rocky trail, with only a flickering candle to point their stumbling way. Today the chambers, open to the public, are lighted by electricity, and the lights are so arranged that the guides, with the use of colored bulbs, produce many surprising and beautiful effects.

When ground waters come to the ceilings of great, empty underground rooms, some evaporation takes place, and a part of the lime which was carried in solution is left clinging to the roof. More water, coming by the same routes and being evaporated in the dry air of the cave, leaves a little more lime, and in time icicle-like forms, or stalactites, develop. At Carlsbad these forms clinging to the ceilings of the caverns are numbered by the thousands. They are all crystalline, and they glisten when illuminated. Some are clear white; others are

275

tinted, green, blue, yellow, or brown, depending upon the mineral matter held in solution. They vary in length from a few inches to ten or even twenty feet. Some are very delicate, less than an inch in diameter, while others are several feet wide at the ceiling and taper to points.

When water coming into a cavern falls to the floor and there evaporates, a little monumentlike form of crystalline limestone, called a stalagmite, is started. As the forms from the ceiling and the floor continue to grow in length, some unite, and we have in the cavern columns of crystal material extending from the floor to the ceiling. Waters flow over the sides of these columns and, as they evaporate, leave a little more lime; thus, some of these columns have become five, ten, and, in a few cases, fifteen feet in diameter.

At places the walls of the cave have become frosted with delicate crystal forms. As the lime is precipitated, it takes on the shapes of kernels of popcorn, or it simulates flowers, such as roses or daffodils. The entire realm is incredibly beautiful, suggestive of some unreal world. One of the chief features of attraction and wonderment in the Carlsbad Caverns is the Temple of the Sun, with huge stalagmite columns rising from floor to ceiling, and hundreds of crystal forms hanging from the roof of the cave in great curtainlike festoons.

The cave is inhabited by about three million bats, and every evening at the sunset hour they begin their customary exodus into the open air. For about three hours they issue from the cave, in long relays, and flit about, gathering night-flying insects, such as moths, beetles, flies, and mosquitoes, until just before the break of dawn, when they re-enter the cave in great

276

swarms. Clinging to the ceilings with their little claws, they hang, head downward, until the following night. All day long the bats remain in complete darkness. They wait for the coming of dusk, and then, at some signal known only to them, they leave the cave for another long, food-gathering flight. It has been estimated from a study of these bats that in one night's foray they consume a little over eleven and one-half tons of flying insects.

MESA VERDE NATIONAL PARK

This green tableland, near the southwestern corner of Colorado, is clothed with piñons and junipers. It is about fifteen miles long and eight miles wide, and it rises abruptly 1,500 feet from the valleys on the north, east, and west. Centuries ago, tribes of peace-loving Indians occupied almost inaccessible homesites on the surface of the mesa. They were basketmakers, and they lived in the region from about the beginning of the Christian era until approximately 700 A.D. Then came a group of Indians who remained until almost 1300 A.D. For a time they lived in pueblos on top of the mesa, and later in well-sheltered caves on the walls of the canyons cut into the mesa. Students of archaeology have found many fascinating records here of the early inhabitants of the Southwest.

It is believed that these dwellings were abandoned about six hundred years ago. The Navajo and Ute Indians, who for many years have lived on the lowlands bordering the mesa, would not visit the cliff dwellings. They feared meeting the spirits of the departed inhabitants of ancient days.

277

The Far View House, built on the surface of the mesa, is one of the best preserved of the pueblo dwellings. There we find living rooms, which are rectangular in shape, and large, circular kivas, which are interpreted as ceremonial halls. In the living rooms there were fireplaces, grinding stones, pottery, and utensils used by the women in their daily household work. The rooms were formerly covered with flat roofs made of poles and clay. The central kiva is thirty-two feet in diameter, and around it are three smaller kivas. This arrangement suggests that each clan had a small kiva of its own, but that the major ceremonies, in which all of the clans engaged jointly, were conducted in the large ceremonial hall.

Cliff Palace might be thought of by white people as the "discovery dwelling." In the summer of 1888, two cowboys, while hunting cattle, came to a point on the brink of a canyon wall, where they stopped to rest their ponies. Looking across the chasm, about fifty feet below the rim in a huge cave, under a great arch of sandstone, they beheld a remarkable array of ancient dwellings. The dwellings in Cliff Palace extend from one end of the cave to the other, a length of about three hundred feet, and the greatest depth of the cave occupied by the palace is one hundred feet. The floor of the cave lies about two hundred feet above the bed of the canyon.

Cliff Palace is reported to be the largest known group of dwellings of its kind. It has at least two hundred living rooms. To provide for the increasing population, second-, third-, and even fourth-story rooms were added. At the south end of the ruin there is a four-story, rectangular tower, which reaches from the floor to the ceiling. The walls of the third-floor room

278

are ornamented with bright-red designs on a white background, a relic of primitive art.

The most remarkable structure in the Palace is a conical tower, about thirty feet in height. Each stone, hewn with the crudest of stone implements, was rounded appropriately for the curvature of the tower, and shaped so as to contribute to its conical form. Twenty-two kivas are located in this dwelling. It is estimated that the living rooms may each have had at least two inhabitants; thus, the population of Cliff Palace is figured at about four hundred. At the north end of the Palace there are grinding bowls, where women knelt and with rounded stones ground corn into meal. Corn was stored in large bins far back under the overhead projecting ledge. In the days of occupancy there may have been a spring to furnish water to the little community, but today there is no easily accessible water. Possibly the disappearance of the springs led to the abandonment of the homes.

In 1906, by an act of Congress, that portion of the mesa which contains the archaeological ruins of historic interest was set aside as a national park. There are more than a score of cliff dwellings and places of special interest in this park. Camps and lodges have been provided for the comfortable accommodation of visitors and a well-trained staff is maintained by the Park Service to serve as guides.

ROCKY MOUNTAIN NATIONAL PARK

This park lies about fifty miles in a straight line northwest of Denver. It includes within its boundaries 405 square miles of some of the most magnificent crest-line peaks in the Front Range of the Rockies in Colorado. The central mountain of scenic interest is Longs Peak, rising in the midst of the Snowy Range to an elevation of 14,255 feet above sea level. There are sixty-five named mountains within the area that reach altitudes of over 10,000 feet.

This region has long been a favorite pleasure ground for people who love to get into high places. It was first established as a national park in 1915, but its boundaries have been adjusted and the park enlarged over and over again in succeeding years. Its eastern gateway is the beautiful village of Estes Park, and from there, over excellent highways, visitors may pass through various portions of the reservation and, if they wish, reach the summit of the range over one of the best modern automobile highways of the West.

Rocky Mountain National Park is a region of special interest to scientists. Here the story of the evolution of the Rocky Mountains, unfolded in our earlier chapters, is clearly reflected: the core rocks of the range are exposed in huge granite masses at many places; on the flanks of the range there are upturned sediments which formerly covered the entire mountain area; at a dozen sites in the park the work of alpine glaciers is recorded; and among the lofty summits are the large amphitheatral basins where those glaciers formed. To the lover of alpine flora or fauna, this is a land of fascination; and to others, a rest cure after a busy year's work in some crowded center of commercial or professional activity. To all who visit the park and come to know its history or the history of plant and animal life in that region, or who simply enjoy the beauty of the landscape, there should come something of inspiration from close contact with some of the wonders of the out-of-door world.

GRAND TETON NATIONAL PARK

The Tetons, of northwestern Wyoming, have been known to white people for a long time. In 1807-08, the intrepid explorer, John Colter, crossed the range on the memorable journey that made him the discoverer of the Yellowstone country. In 1811, it was visited by the Astorians, who crossed through this part of the West on their expedition to the mouth of the Columbia, but not until 1929 was this range of magnificent mountain scenery set aside as a national park.

William H. Jackson, who brought home from the West the first good photographic records, was in this region in 1872, and he is reported to have taken the first photographs of the Tetons. Thomas Moran, the famous landscape artist, first painted the Teton Range in 1879. Mountain climbers have sought this region because the peaks provide a challenge to the most skillful, and the record of mountain climbing in this park contains many a tragedy. The first scaling of the major Teton peak was accomplished in 1898. By 1930, they had all been scaled.

The center of interest in this park is the twenty-seven miles of the front range of the Tetons, lying in a north-south line. At their east base, in a heavily forested zone, there is a chain of small lakes, each with a beautiful setting. At the north is Leigh Lake; then come String and Jenny, and farther south are Bradley, Taggart, and Phelps Lakes. They are all held in by frontal moraines built up at the terminal positions of alpine glaciers, which descended eastward from large catchment basins in the summit region of this mountain area. The park includes, in addition to the mountain range, a considerable portion of the low, nearly level lands to the east. Adjoining the park at the east, is a large area in the valley of the Snake River, which has been set aside as a national monument. Thus, the approach to the mountains has been preserved, and from this outlying level land may be obtained many of the most arresting scenic views.

Trails have been built through certain of the canyons, so that those who enjoy life in the saddle may travel far into the range, camp among the lofty summits, and, by crossing a divide, descend by some other trail to the lowlands. Those who wish may climb the front face of the range on well-built trails to points where ancient glacial records are clearly shown, where tiny icefields may be visited, and where close-ups of the mighty mountains may be enjoyed in perfect safety. There is no need of risking one's life to see and enjoy the Tetons; in fact, those who see them from a little distance probably gain much more of inspirational value than those who scale the rugged mountains.

YELLOWSTONE NATIONAL PARK

This park may be thought of as the ancestor of all our parks, and as the source of the idea of national parks. While John Colter was the first white man to set foot in this region, he did not see all the wonders of Yellowstone Park; at least, he missed the geysers, and he may not have seen the gorgeously colored Grand Canyon of the Yellowstone. In 1870 a well-organized exploring party visited this section, and it was at one of their evening campfire powwows that the idea was first expressed that it should be made a national reservation for the enjoyment of all the people. It was through the efforts of those men that the area was set aside, in 1872, by an act signed by President Grant, as our first national park—in fact, the first national park in the world.

Little by little, through the eighties and the nineties, and since then, this park has been made more and more easily accessible to millions of tourists. Highways have been constructed; comfortable hotels, lodges, camp grounds, and cafeterias are available for visitors. Public entertainment is provided on lecture platforms, and personally conducted tours are now arranged to the geysers, to the rim of the canyon, to the mud pots, hot springs, mud volcanoes, through the forests and woodlands, and to the feeding grounds of the big grizzlies. Well-trained, experienced instructors serve during the summers as guides, just as in other national parks, for all who wish to learn of the history and science associated with these wonderlands.

The Yellowstone Park area is in the midst of the Rocky Mountains of northwest Wyoming. To the east is the Absaroka Range; at the northwest are the Gallatin Mountains. Much of the central portion of the park is a lava plateau, and the deeper layers of the moulten rocks that poured out into this region long ago are not yet entirely cool. The waters from underground come to the surface as hot springs at varying temperatures, up to the boiling point, and at places they erupt intermittently as geysers. Some of the geysers are very irregular in their eruptions, but Old Faithful continues to make a grand display once in about every sixty-seven minutes. Year in and year out, the announcements of the next eruption of Old Faithful are made in the hotels, dining halls, cafeterias, and all tourist camps. As the time of eruption draws near, throngs gather about the low cone which this geyser has built up above its own opening or throat. Soon the waters begin to sputter and rise five or six feet. With each impulse, coming from a subterranean explosion, the water is thrown a little higher, until at its best it spurts about 120 feet in the air. Great clouds of mist form and drift off with the wind. The geyser plays for about four minutes, and in the closing stages gets lower and lower. With each eruption some of the heated waters, which bring silica or quartz material in solution, flow over the rim of the little crater and down the slope of the low cone. As the water cools, the silica is precipitated, and thus the cone becomes a little larger.

Months could be spent here without duplicating the lessons in geology, physiography, botany, or zoology. Years could be spent by an artist, sketching or painting from rivaling points of beauty. No one should leave the park without visiting outlook stations on the rim of the Grand Canyon for a view of the famous Lower Falls of the Yellowstone River in their picturesque setting. The stream, as it flows in a broad, shallow valley from Yellowstone Lake, is peaceful; but as the gradient increases, rapids and cascades develop in the course; the valley becomes narrower and deeper, and at the Upper Falls the waters leap about forty feet through the air; soon the stream plunges 273 feet into the lower portion of a beautiful V-shaped gorge, which it has cut into the lava plateau. From the base of the Lower Falls, the stream hurries on to the northward in so narrow a channel that the waters are crowded. In time the Yellowstone joins the Missouri River. The walls of this canyon, all composed of volcanic rock, are highly colored in shades of red, brown, and yellow. As the volcanic rocks disintegrate, oxidation takes place, and, in the presence of heated vapors, the various colors common to the oxides of iron come to life. The canyon walls, rising 1,000 to 1,200 feet from the stream channel, are very steep, and at places exceedingly rugged.

Each of our national parks and each of those in the Canadian Rockies has its charm, but there is perhaps more of varied interest in Yellowstone than in any other one park. It is unique in having on exhibition so many of the secondary phenomena of volcanism and such brilliant coloring in the volcanic rocks.

WIND CAVE NATIONAL PARK

Tom Bingham, while hunting for deer in 1881, at the southeast margin of the Black Hills, happened upon a curious hole in the rocks, from which wind was escaping. The story goes that when he leaned over the hole for a closer look, still sitting in his saddle, his hat was blown from his head. He returned to camp that evening, told his story, and the other men jeered at him. He insisted that they go to the spot with him the next morning, to check on the truth of his tale. They rode up to

285

the same opening in the rocks, dismounted, and were leaning over to peep into the hole, when Tom really lost his hat, for this time it was sucked into the hole. He was laughed at, but with restraint. This strange phenomenon revealed to Tom and his companions has occurred over and over again. I have myself visited the place and I know that the winds change, coming out from underground at times, and rushing in at other times. This shifting of the wind is believed to be caused by changes in atmospheric pressure in the air outside the cave. When the barometer is falling, the wind usually blows outward; when it is rising, the wind blows inward.

Curiosity led the pioneer men to find a way into the underground realm, and there they discovered, much to their surprise, a strange and beautiful crystal fairyland. The walls of the caverns are frosted over with delicately colored forms of lime and gypsum, some arranged in honeycomb patterns. Tiny white crystals appear on a pink background, occasionally hanging in clusters from the ceilings and from ledges on the cavern walls, in decorative designs of rare beauty.

At least ten miles of underground passageways have been explored. At one place the crystals of gypsum hang as fine, hairlike threads, which will swing if blown upon with the breath. They are twelve to eighteen inches in length, and are called "Noah's Beard." Some patches are frosted with curlicue embossings and sculpturesque ice blossoms. No large stalactites or stalagmites, such as those in the Carlsbad Caverns, are found here. This is a region where the waters coming into the dry air of the cave evaporate on the walls without dripping, and the crystals form a coating, or veneer, on the walls. It is

286

a place well worth visiting, and it is open to the public every day throughout the year. Well-trained guides are available at stated intervals to take parties through the many corridors and galleries and point out the various crystal forms.

Wind Cave was established as a national park in 1903. It includes nearly 12,000 acres, but a part of the area is maintained as a game preserve for buffalo, elk, antelope, and deer, which range in complete freedom. The animals are so tame that they may frequently be seen from the main highway.

GLACIER NATIONAL PARK

In 1895 our government purchased from the Blackfoot Indians for $1,500,000 their rights to the territory east of the Continental Divide in the region of the Lewis and Clark Range in Montana. The land was bought in order to throw it open to prospectors and miners, but the region has not proved to be highly mineralized, and therefore mining in this section of the Rockies has been of very little importance. About 1900 George Bird Grinnell, an enthusiastic lover of the wilderness, later president of the National Parks Association, published an article in the *Century Magazine,* in which he called attention to the exceptional grandeur and beauty in this portion of the Rocky Mountain front range. Ten years later, President Taft signed a bill creating Glacier National Park. Since then, hundreds of thousands of people have visited the reservation; many are satisfied to go by motor to the beautiful camps and hotels located on the shores of lakes situated in the foothill approaches, or to cross the high mountain area in a car. Others follow the trails, afoot or on horseback, and thus come closer to the high mountains and sheer rock cliffs that characterize the region. They travel slowly and for hours through beautiful forests, see wild game at close range, and, as they rise higher, enjoy magnificent alpine gardens, hardly surpassed anywhere in the world. In time they come into the summit areas, where there are perennial snow fields and true glaciers. The park contains about fifteen hundred square miles, and within its boundaries there are more than sixty small glaciers, and at least two hundred exquisite mountain lakes.

In our story of the making of great mountain ranges, this region was referred to as an example of an area where faulting has taken place on a grand scale. This is the section where huge mountain ranges, really all that there is in this park, and more that has since been worn away, moved eastward over the western margin of the Great Plains. Those who are interested may have the fault line, where it comes to the surface, pointed out to them by the ranger naturalists, for they are all specially trained for their work in the park, and, knowing its geologic history, will readily designate Chief Mountain as the "discovery location" of the famous Lewis Overthrust Fault.

In this national park many are disappointed at not finding more glaciers. What are left there are but tiny remnants of glaciers that formerly extended fifteen, twenty, or thirty miles down the canyons and to the foothills of the mountain range. They gouged out the deep troughs in which the long mountain lakes, such as St. Mary's, Sherburne, McDonald, Logging, Quartz, Bowman, Kintla, and Waterton are located, leaving the morainic dams that hold these waters in as lakes.

288

The Canadian people have set aside an area adjoining Glacier National Park on the north as Waterton Lakes Park. In 1932 the Waterton-Glacier International Peace Park was dedicated. Thus, the two adjacent parks were united under a common name, a reflection of the friendship between the peoples living north and south of the political boundary line.

Many who visit Glacier National Park find in the midst of this magnificent display of mountain scenery a marvelous variety of flowers. If you are high above timber line, among the hardy plants, such as the mosses and lichens, during the summer you will find many of the delicately colored alpine flowers. Lower on the mountain slopes are heather, gentians, wild heliotrope, and stunted trees of alpine fir, whitebark pine, and alpine larch. In the valleys, deep in the heart of the range, where many of the trails are located, one passes among Engelmann's spruce, alpine fir, lodgepole pine, Douglas fir, and limber pine. For the most part these forests consist of red cedar and hemlock, with many larch, fir, spruce, and white pine.

THE CANADIAN NATIONAL PARKS IN THE ROCKY MOUNTAINS

The Canadians have been exceedingly generous to all the people of their country, and to all the world, in setting aside large areas of their Rocky Mountains as national reservations. The Waterton Lakes Park, just north of the Montana line, established in 1895, is comparatively small. It contains 220 square miles, but the chain of national parks farther north includes virtually all of the Front Range for more than 250 miles. This area is divided into four different parks: Kootenay,

Yoho, Banff, and Jasper. The first two are relatively small, but Jasper, established in 1907, contains 4,200 square miles, and Banff, established in 1885, contains about 2,500 square miles.

For a long time lovers of rugged mountain country and zealous alpinists visited this region on foot, or on horseback, and with pack trains. There is a network of interesting trails through this mountain country, with plenty of opportunity to get the thrills of life in wilderness wonderlands, far away from the sounds of locomotives or automobiles and all the noises of our modern conventional life. Moreover, the Canadian people have now built a number of excellent automobile highways, which make travel through much of the park very easy. Bus service is available during normal times, and thousands of tourists have been taken, from the railway stations on the Canadian Pacific or from the Canadian National, to points of particular interest, or to camps where they elect to spend a summer season.

The Canadian parks are remarkable in many respects. Those who would like to see how mountains are made, how in the movements that take place the huge layers of rock are contorted into anticlines and synclines, and how they are broken and crushed as they move slowly upward, and in this case eastward, may see examples of these phenomena from the saddle, or from the seat of an open car. There is probably no inland body of water that surpasses, in beauty of setting, Lake Louise, forty-seven miles into the mountains from Banff. There is no other place easily accessible in North America where large glaciers and a huge icefield can so readily be visited as in the

290

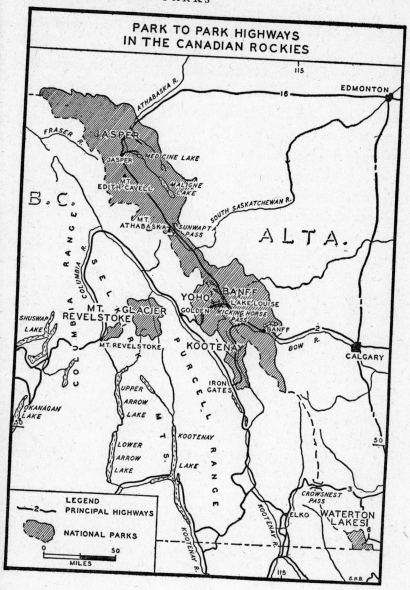

PARK TO PARK HIGHWAYS
IN THE CANADIAN ROCKIES

291

Remnants of glaciers in Glacier National Park.

A deep trough in the Glacier National Park. The deep trough was once occupied by ice, and the lake is held in by morainic material in the low forested area. The ancient sedimentary rocks in this portion of Glacier National Park are nearly horizontal.

A huge glacial boulder brought from the Absaroka Range westward across the area where the canyon of the Yellowstone has since been excavated.

region of Mt. Athabaska and the Columbia Icefield. These places are now within walking distance from points on the Jasper-Banff Highway. A circuit may be taken, when gasoline is available, from Calgary into the mountains at Banff, by side trips into the Kootenay and Yoho Parks, northward for nearly 200 miles to Jasper, then eastward to Edmonton, and thence, by an interesting road, over the Great Plains back to Calgary. Some day that will become one of the famous automobile circuits of western Canada.

There is more to see in these great reservations than anyone can absorb on a single journey—mountain structures, mountain flora, and mountain fauna. There is wild game in these parks surpassing anything easily available to the lovers of the out-of-doors who cannot organize great pack-train expeditions into wilderness regions. Here it is comparatively easy to see in their native haunts the Rocky Mountain goat, elk, moose, mule, deer; black, brown, and grizzly bear; cougar, and coyote. Among the smaller mammals found are the Columbian ground squirrel or picket-pin gopher, mantled ground squirrel, which resembles a chipmunk, yellow-haired porcupine, snowshoe rabbit, red squirrel, marten, muskrat, pike, and hoary marmot, or "whistler." Beavers also are numerous, particularly near Banff.

Those whose eyes are focused more acutely on the plant life find that the highway is at places cut through magnificent forests, and appears to be in a canyon, for the trees are straight and tall and rise as vertical walls on either side of the new motor route. There the visitor will see white and black spruce, balsam fir, Engelmann's spruce, Douglas fir, limber or Rocky

293

Mountain pine, Lyall's larch, white birch, alpine fir, and aspen. Many varieties of shrubs also grow on the mountain slopes. There are some who may prefer the wild flowering plants of the wilderness region. Here there is a revelation for the visitor, for the valleys and mountain slopes are clothed in a riot of color. More than five hundred varieties have been identified. Near the snow line there are waves of blue, rose, white and yellow. Among the best-known species are larkspur, violet, columbine, Indian paintbrush, alpine anemone, harebell, snow lily, gentian, aster, everlasting, mountain heather, hellebore, saxifrage, dryas, vetch, wintergreen, and fireweed.

Those more hardy individuals who will spend a few days in the saddle and camp out in a wilderness region may visit some of the most beautiful high-mountain country in the world, areas that cannot be seen from the roadways. They will have a series of "close-up," intimate experiences never to be forgotten.

West of the great chain of Front Range parks in the Rocky Mountains of Canada, two other areas have been set aside as reservations because of their scientific and inspirational value. Glacier National Park of Canada is located in the Selkirk Range, within the great northern bend of the Columbia River. It contains over 500 square miles and its snow-capped peaks, glaciers, and luxuriant flora make it a region that someday, when it is more easily accessible, will attract many visitors.

A little farther west, but still in that great northward bend of the Columbia and on the western slopes of the Selkirks, is Mt. Revelstoke Park, now accessible by motor road. It was established in 1914 and contains about 100 square miles. It is another choice bit of mountain landscape where hundreds of people find rest and recreation in comfortable camping spots during their vacation periods.

THE DENVER MOUNTAIN PARKS

West of the city of Denver, in the Front Range of the Rocky Mountains, there has been established by the people in the capital city of Colorado a park which they think of as their own, but maintain for all who wish to come. It is open to the public, and there, at elevations up to 10,000 feet above sea level, you may find excellent camp grounds, hotels, and outlook stations that are easily accessible on good highways.

This park is not in the lofty portion of the Front Range, but · lies at intermediate levels, where there are beautiful grasslands bordered by forests, where the streams provide abundant opportunity for fishing, where the hillsides have many trails and nature walks, and where, in the colder season of the year, thousands of young people go for winter sports. At the western margin is Mt. Evans, 14,260 feet above sea level, one of the superb peaks of the Rockies. Its summit can be reached during the summer on an automobile highway, and it rewards the visitor with a rich expanse of magnificent mountain panoramas to the north, west, and south. The outlook to the east is over the foothill belt, and far over the western margin of the Great Plains, where the city of Denver is located. Each year thousands of people think of the Denver Mountain Parks as places where they will spend their vacation periods in the summer or winter, and where they may conveniently spend weekends,

295

or even commute for business duties in the near-by cities among the foothills or in Denver.

WHY NATIONAL PARKS?

The establishment of national parks in the wilderness areas of the world, or in the natural wonderlands and beauty spots, or where any unmarred bits of nature remain, provides cultural opportunities of inestimable value. The movement, which started in the United States, has spread throughout the Americas, and to a few of the older nations beyond the seas. With the great industrialization of modern life, with the mechanization and commercialization of farming and ranching, with the intensity that characterizes the work of many professional people, with the speed, hustle, and bustle of our everyday lives during most of the year, there should be some time and some place for real relaxation, for recreation, for rest, and for inspiration. The national parks offer all this to those who long to place themselves in sympathy with nature.

> To him who in the love of Nature holds
> Communion with her visible forms, she speaks
> A various language; for his gayer hours
> She has a voice of gladness, and a smile
> And eloquence of beauty, and she glides
> Into his darker musings, with a mild
> And healing sympathy, that steals away
> Their sharpness, ere he is aware. . . .
>
> *Thanatopsis*—WILLIAM CULLEN BRYANT

CROSS-SECTION DRAWINGS

Based upon field studies by the author
and prepared for reproduction by

DR. ERWIN RAISZ

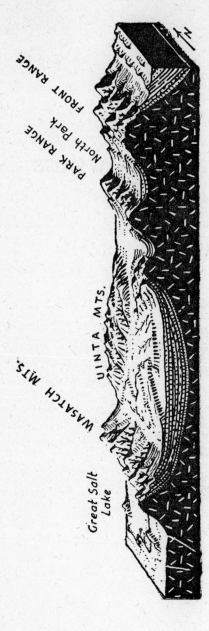

I. Simplified structure section near the north border of Colorado.

Crossing the Rocky Mountain area near the northern border of Colorado, we find the conditions in the field as shown in this drawing. In the foothill belt east of the Front Range the formations are upturned so that there are hogback ridges. The Front Range stands up conspicuously with core-rocks of the ancient complex. We next cross North Park, a basin being filled with waste material washed from the mountains. West of the Park Range we come to the Uinta Mountains, which extend from east to west. We could not show the structure of this range in the drawing. It is a huge anticline. Finally we reach the Wasatch Mountains. This range is a great fault block. It has risen above the general level of the country during a late mountain-making period along a fracture plain shown at the west base of the range.

BIG HORN BASIN

CENTRAL RANGE
Cloud Peak 13,165

LIMESTONE
BASTIONS

FLATIRONS

GREAT PLAINS

N

II. East-west structure section of the Big Horn Range, Wyoming.

The Big Horn Range of north central Wyoming, which appears also on Page 303, is a great anticlinal fold. The layers of sedimentary rock which appear to the east and to the west formerly went over the top of the range. They have been removed by stream and glacial erosion. In the heart of the range the core-rocks now appear at various places. If all the rock material that has been removed from this great fold were replaced, the summit of the arch would be at least 10,000 feet higher than the present crest-line of the range.

III. East-west structure section of the Grand Teton Range, western Wyoming.

The Tetons, which have been set aside as a National Park in the northwestern part of Wyoming, are carved out of a huge block of the crustal portion of the earth which has been thrust upwards at least 7,000 feet. The fissure along which the movement took place is at the east base of the range. The sedimentary rocks to the west of the range formerly extended over the summit. They have been removed by weathering and erosion. Glaciers formed in this range and those that descended to the east base left the moraines which help to form the modern lake basins.

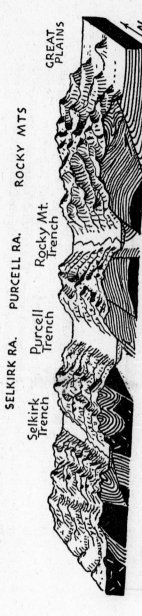

SELKIRK RA.   PURCELL RA.   ROCKY MTS

Selkirk
Trench

Purcell
Trench

Rocky Mt.
Trench

GREAT
PLAINS

N

IV. Simplified structure section of the Rockies near the International Boundary Line.

At the international boundary line between the United States and Canada the structure of the Rocky Mountains is exceedingly complex. This drawing is based upon field work carried out by Dr. Reginald A. Daly of Harvard. At the east are the great plains with horizontal structure. The Rocky Mountain Front Range rises abruptly several thousand feet into the air. It was moved eastward by thrust faulting. Then comes the Rocky Mountain trench where faulting caused a portion of the earth to collapse. In the ranges to the west the rocks are very much folded, contorted, and faulted. We pass range after range and one trench after another. Some of the long trenches contain the beautiful lakes of British Columbia.

V. The Black Canyon of the Gunnison in Colorado.

The field conditions as shown in this drawing indicate that the Gunnison River has cut a magnificent canyon, which is about two thousand feet deep, through layers of lava into the complex pre-Cambrian core-rocks of an ancient mountain range. The river, when locating itself on the original surface, did not know what it would encounter in lowering its channel at this particular place. It is a superimposed stream. The fantastic features on the walls of the Black Canyon of the Gunnison are due to the weathering of the pre-Cambrian complex of rocks.

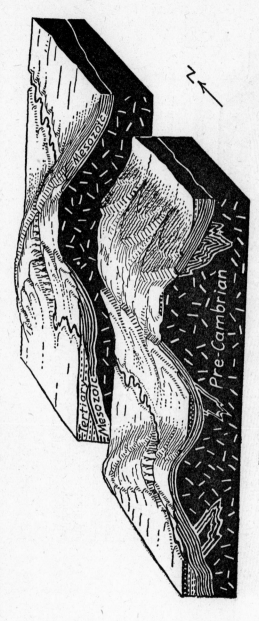

Tertiary Mesozoic Pre-Cambrian

VI. The gorges of the Big Horn River in central Wyoming.

In this drawing, which presents the field conditions in north central Wyoming, we can see a large river, the Big Horn, cutting a deep gorge through a small anticlinal mountain range at the left and then proceeding northward near the west base of the Big Horn Range until it suddenly changes its course and turns directly eastward through the Big Horn Mountains. That river must have been located on a surface now washed away, which was high above these two mountain ranges. As the stream lowered its course below its former location, it was presented the task of cutting directly across two mountain ranges which had been buried. It is a superimposed stream. Almost all the magnificent gorges in the Rocky Mountains have been cut by superimposed streams.

VII. The gorge of the North Platte near Casper, Wyoming.

Near Casper in central Wyoming the North Platte River has cut a very picturesque gorge. Long ago the tertiary sediments of this locality are depicted in this drawing. Long ago the tertiary sediments mantled most of the country. Just a few hills rose above that material. The rivers were located on the surface of those tertiary sediments, and at this place the stream, as it lowered its course, cutting a great canyon, had a series of remarkable adventures. The soft tertiary sands and gravels were removed very easily, then the river found a series of Paleozoic and Mesozoic sedimentary rocks that were part of an ancient and buried mountain. As the stream lowered its channel it cut into the old core-rocks of the mountain range.

COLORADO PLATEAU   ROCKY MOUNTAINS   GREAT

Carrizo Mts   Mesa Verde   San Juan Mts.   Salida   SOUTH PARK   Pikes Peak   PLAINS

Garden of the Gods

VIII. Simplified structure section from the Garden of the Gods, Colorado, southwest to the Colorado Plateau in Arizona.

In crossing the Rocky Mountain region from the Garden of the Gods in Colorado southwestward to the Colorado Plateau of Arizona, we should find the field conditions as reflected in this drawing. Where we start, the rocks are upturned as they appear in the Garden of the Gods. There they stand on edge. In Pikes Peak and the Front Range the core-rocks, chiefly of granite, appear at the surface and produce a picturesque landscape. Then we cross lowland parks and parallel mountain ranges until we come to the Great Dome of the San Juan Mountains in southwestern Colorado. On the west side of that we find the layers of rock turned up nearly on edge again. A little farther west the layers of rock are nearly horizontal as in the Mesa Verde, the famous home of the cliff dwellers. In the Carrizo Mountains we cross an extinct or dormant volcano.

GEOLOGIC CALENDAR FOR THE ROCKY MOUNTAIN REGION

On the following page appears the Geologic Calendar for the Rocky Mountain Region. For chronological order, read this table from the bottom up. It epitomizes (and generalizes) the story of the periods, the story of the rocks, and the story of the mountain-forming uplifts.

Era	Period	Rock Materials	Chief Events
Psychozoic or Recent Era Lasted about 20 million years	Post-glacial	Stream deposits Sand dunes Peat in bogs and swamps	Vigorous stream action Glaciers shrinking Winds active Mountain growth continues
	Pleistocene "The Great Ice Age"	Glacial moraines Sand and gravel deposits Stream deposits	Alpine glaciers in all high mountains Moraines deposited Lake basins formed Ice-front lakes All streams flooded Mountain growth continues
Cenozoic or Modern Era Lasted about 60 million years	Pliocene	Vast amounts of stream deposits Volcanic outpourings Volcanic ash	Great mountain growth Peneplanation of large areas Widespread filling of basins
	Miocene	Stream deposits Lake deposits Volcanic materials	Mountains being worn down Volcanic eruptions
	Oligocene	Stream deposits Lake deposits Volcanic materials	Mountains being worn down Volcanic eruptions
	Eocene	Stream deposits Glacial moraines	Active erosion in mountains Glaciation in mountains Mountain growth continuing
Mesozoic or Medieval Era Lasted about 110 million years	Upper Cretaceous	Mesa Verde sandstone, a widespread mesa-capping Dakota sandstone, a great hogback maker Shales, conglomerates, coal	Great mountain growth Birth of Rocky Mountains Volcanic activity
	Lower Cretaceous	Sandstones, shales, conglomerates, limestones	Periods of sedimentation in the Rocky Mountain region
	Jurassic	Sandstones, shales, conglomerates	
	Triassic	Red sandstones, red shales, conglomerates	

GEOLOGIC CALENDAR FOR THE ROCKY MOUNTAIN REGION.—*Cont.*

Era	Period	Rock Materials	Chief Events
Paleozoic or Ancient Era — Lasted about 330 million years	Permian	The lower or older Red Beds	Making of many of the Red Beds
	Carboniferous Devonian Silurian Ordovician Cambrian	Represented in Rocky Mountains by limestones, shales, sandstones, conglomerates	In general, a long period of sedimentation in the Rocky Mountain region. The ocean waters invade this area several times Areas of accumulation shift Some crustal movements

pre-Cambrian Eras — Lasted about 1000 million years		The fundamental or pre-Cambrian complex
		The core rocks in many of the mountain ranges
		Rocks include:
		  schists
		  gneisses
		  quartzites
		  slates
		Granitic intrusions:
		  many dark intrusives
		  some little altered
		  sedimentary formations
			During these very long eras there were several mountain-making periods, great vulcanism, long periods of erosion, and, at some places in the world, glaciation
			A complex history, never to be worked out in detail

BIBLIOGRAPHY

For the National Parks
General Reports

Ashton, Ruth E. *Plants of Rocky Mountain National Park.* U. S. Department of the Interior, National Park Service; U. S. Government Printing Office, Washington, 1933.

Bailey, Harold E. and Virginia Long. *Forests and Trees of the Western National Parks.* Conservation Bulletin No. 6; U. S. Government Printing Office, Washington, D. C., 1941.

Beals, Ralph L. *Ethnology of Rocky Mountain National Park; The Ute and Arapaho.* U. S. Department of the Interior, National Park Service, Field Division of Education, Berkeley, California, January, 1935.

Beals, Ralph L. *History of Glacier National Park, with Particular Emphasis on the Northern Developments.* U. S. Department of the Interior, National Park Service, Field Division of Education, Berkeley, California, 1935.

Effinger, William L. *The Geology of Rocky Mountain National Park.* U. S. Department of the Interior, National Park Service, Field Division of Education, Berkeley, California, 1934.

Rensch, H. E. *Historical Background for the Rocky Mountain National Park.* U. S. Department of the Interior, National Park Service, Field Division of Education, February, Berkeley, California, 1935.

Schultz, Leonard P. *Fishes of Glacier National Park Montana.* National Park Service, U. S. Government Printing Office, Washington, 1941.

Smith, Baxter L. *The Zoology of Rocky Mountain National Park.* U. S. Department of the Interior, National Park Service, Field Division of Education, Berkeley, California, 1935.

Story, Isabelle F. *Glimpses of Our National Parks.* National Park Service, U. S. Government Printing Office, Washington, 1941. Copy for the original (1915) edition of *Glimpses of Our National Parks* was prepared by Robert Sterling Yard, who, in 1920, resigned as Editor of the National Park Service.

Wright, George M., Dixon, Joseph S., and Thompson, Ben H. *Fauna of the National Parks of the United States*. U. S. Department of the Interior, National Park Service, Contribution of Wild Life Survey, Fauna Series No. I—May, 1932, U. S. Government Printing Office, Washington, 1933.

Guide Books

The National Park Service has issued and has available a guide book for each of the National Parks. Copies can be obtained by addressing the National Park Headquarters now in the Merchandise Mart, Chicago, 54, Illinois. After the war the office will probably be returned to Washington, D. C.

Canadian National Parks

Hornaday, William T. *Camp-fires in the Canadian Rockies*. Charles Scribner's Sons, New York, 1906.

MacKay, B. R. *Geology of the National Parks of Canada in the Rockies and Selkirks*. Reprinted from *Canadian Geographical Journal*. National Parks Bureau, Department of Mines and Resources, Ottawa, Canada.

National Parks of Canada, The: National Parks Bureau, Department of Mines and Resources, Ottawa, Canada, 1938.

Niven, Frederick J. *Colour in the Canadian Rockies*. Nelson (Toronto); 1937.

Palmer, Howard and Thorington, J. Monroe. *A Climber's Guide to the Rocky Mountains of Canada*. Third ed. The American Alpine Club, 1940.

Thorington, J. Monroe. *The Glittering Mountains of Canada*. John W. Lea, Philadelphia, Pa., 1925.

Williams, M. B. *Through the Heart of the Rockies and Selkirks*. Pub. under direction of Hon. Charles Stewart, Minister of the Interior, Ottawa, Canada, 1929.

General Books

Coulter, John M. *New Manual of Botany of the Central Rocky Mountains* (Rev. Ed.). American Book Company, New York, 1909.

Fritz, Percy Stanley. *Colorado, The Centennial State.* Prentice-Hall, Inc., New York, 1941.

Fryxell, Fritiof. *The Tetons: Interpretations of a Mountain Landscape.* University of California Press, Berkeley, 1938.

Johnson, Overton and Winter, Wm. H. *Route Across the Rocky Mountains.* Reprinted with Preface and Notes by Carl L. Cannon, from the edition of 1846, Princeton University Press, Princeton, 1932.

Lomax, John A., ed. *Cowboy Songs and Other Frontier Ballads.* Revised and Enlarged, Collected by John A. and Alan Lomax, New York, The Macmillan Company, 1938.

Melbo, Irving R. *Our Country's National Parks.* 2 Vols. The Bobbs-Merrill Company, New York, 1941.

Preston, Richard J., Jr. *Rocky Mountain Trees.* Iowa State College Press, Ames, Iowa, 1940.

Thwaites, Reuben Gold. *A Brief History of Rocky Mountain Exploration.* D. Appleton and Company, New York, 1914.

Van Name, Willard G. *Vanishing Forest Reserves.* The Gorham Press, Boston, 1929.

Villard, Henry. *The Past and Present of the Pike's Peak Gold Regions.* Reprinted from edition of 1860 with Introduction and Notes by LeRoy R. Hafen. Princeton University Press, Princeton, 1932.

Yard, Robert Sterling. *The Book of the National Parks.* Charles Scribner's Sons, New York, 1919.

Yard, Robert Sterling. *Our Federal Lands.* Charles Scribner's Sons, New York, 1928.

Mining History

Fritz, Percy Stanley. *Colorado, The Centennial State.* Prentice-Hall, New York, 1941.

Henderson, Charles W. "Mining in Colorado." U. S. Geological Survey, Professional Paper 138. Government Printing Office, Washington, D. C., 1926.

Minerals Yearbook, Review of 1940. U. S. Dept. of Interior, Bureau of Mines. Washington, D. C.; Government Printing Office, 1941. (This series, published annually, contains a wealth of very valuable material bearing upon the mining industry.)

Mines Register, Volume 21. Atlas Publishing Company, New York, 1942. (Published annually; contains important statistical material and recent reports.)

O'Connor, Harvey. *The Guggenheims*. Covici-Friede, New York, 1937.

Rickard, T. A. *A History of American Mining*. McGraw-Hill, New York, 1932.

"The Diamond Fraud." *Engineering and Mining Journal*, 1872 (Dec. 10), Vol. 14, No. 24, pp. 379-380.

"The True Story of the Camp Bird Discovery." *Engineering and Mining Journal*, 1910 (June 18), Vol. 89, No. 25, p. 1266.

White, T. "Snipers Gold." *North American Review*, 1933 (Oct.), Vol. 236, No. 4, pp. 329-337.

Maps of the National Parks

Bryce Canyon National Park. Shown on Kanab Quadrangle. Size, 16½" x 20". Scale, 1:125,000.

Carlsbad Caverns National Park. Map in preparation.

Glacier National Park, Montana. Size, 31" x 35". Scale, 1:125,000.

Grand Canyon National Park—
East Half Size, 41" x 46". Scale, 1:48,000.
West Half Size, 44" x 47". Scale, 1:48,000.

Grand Teton National Park. Shown on Grand Teton sheet. Size, 16½" x 20". Scale, 1:125,000.

Mesa Verde National Park, Colorado. Size, 31" x 46". Scale, 1:31,250.

Rocky Mountain National Park, Colorado. Size, 16½" x 20". Scale, 1:125,000.

Wind Cave National Park, S. Dakota. Shown on Harney Peak and Hermosa Topographic Sheets. Size, 16½" x 20". Scale, 1:125,000.

Yellowstone National Park, Wyoming—Montana—Idaho. Size, 32" x 36". Scale, 1:125,000.

Zion National Park, Utah. Shown on Kanab and St. George Quadrangles. Size, 16½" x 20". Scale, 1:125,000. Note: New map in course of publication.

Recreational areas of the United States published by National Park Service of the Department of the Interior. 31½" x 42". Scale, 1" equals approximately 75 miles.

INDEX

317

319

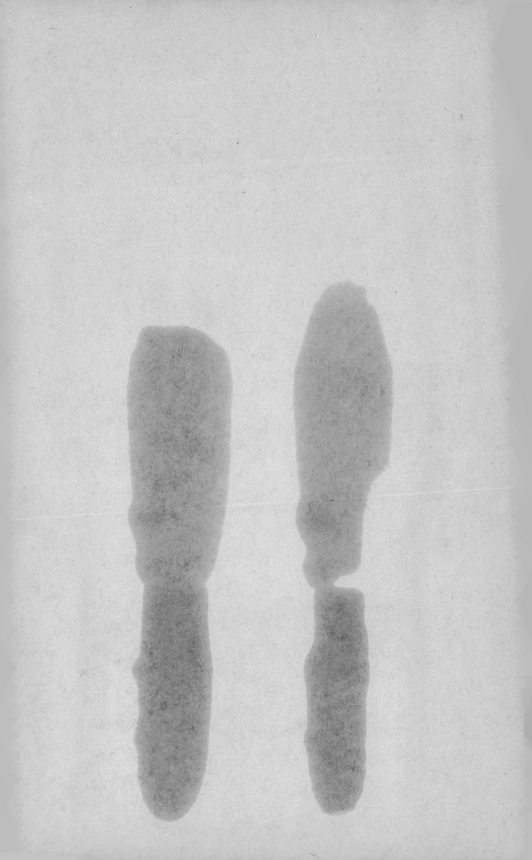

26543

F
721
.A8

ATWOOD, WALLACE W.
THE ROCKY MOUNTAINS.

DATE DUE	
MAY 0 1 1994	
FEB 23 1999	

GAYLORD   PRINTED IN U.S.A.